PELICAN BOOKS

A833

MATHEMATICS IN MANAGEMENT

Albert Battersby was born in 1917 and graduated as a chemist in 1939. However, he spent most of the war on operational air-crew duties with the Royal Air Force. Since the war he has been the manager of factories in Brazil, India, and the United Kingdom. He has been interested in modern methods of management, including operational research and work study, and was responsible for one of the earliest applications of electronic computers to production control.

Albert Battersby was a senior lecturer at the College of Aeronautics, Cranfield, before being elected a Fellow of Balliol in 1966, and he has an international reputation as a consultant, lecturer, and broadcaster on management. He is the author of *A Guide to Stock Control* (1962) and *Network Analysis* (1964). Both books have been translated into other languages and a fourth book, on sales forecasting, is in the press.

D0683166

02.

Albert Battersby

Mathematics
in Management

Penguin Books

Penguin Books Ltd, Harmondsworth, Middlesex, England
Penguin Books Inc., 7110 Ambassador Road, Baltimore, Maryland 21207, U.S.A.
Penguin Books Australia Ltd, Ringwood, Victoria, Australia

—

First Published 1966
Reprinted 1968

—

Copyright © Albert Battersby, 1966

—

Made and printed in Great Britain by
Hazell Watson & Viney Ltd,
Aylesbury, Bucks
Set in Monotype Imprint

TO RUTH

Contents

Acknowledgements

I AM indebted to Jonathan Cape Ltd for permission to reproduce the poem 'Business Men' by Louis MacNeice in the heading of Chapter 1. Parts of Chapters 4 and 7 appeared originally in *The Accountant* and *The Manager* respectively, and I am grateful to the editors and publishers of these journals for permission to use this material. The diagram from *Industrial Dynamics* by Jay Forrester in Chapter 7 is reproduced by permission of the publishers, John Wiley and the M.I.T. Press, and the author. The computing for Chapter 8 was done by the service bureau of De La Rue Bull Machines Ltd, and my thanks are due not only to that company as a whole but also to Ian McNaught-Davis, Michael Nichols and Charles Kehela for their personal interest. Frank Houseman and Trevor Russell did most of the hard work behind the case example in Chapter 2, with the willing cooperation of the Department of Flight at Cranfield. Practically every member of the staff of Cranfield Work Study School has helped in some way, especially John Johnson and Myra Ellis. The typing was done with patience and good humour by my wife and Ann Smith. My friend and colleague John O'Shaughnessy read the drafts of the manuscript and gave me much helpful advice.

Above all, I have to thank Warwick Sawyer, whose skilful criticism as the consultant editor was combined with a most human and friendly approach, Eric Duckworth, and those correspondents who, by pointing out errors and offering constructive criticism, have helped to improve this second impression.

I

The Innumerate Nation

The two men talking business
So easily in the train
Project themselves upon me
Just as the window pane

Reflects their faces, and I
Find myself in a trance
To hear two strangers talking
The same language for once.

LOUIS MACNEICE, *Business Men*

THE AGE OF COMPLEXITY

THE big business organization as we know it today did not
exist in the early nineteenth century. A hundred years ago even
the largest companies were directed in all but their most
trivial aspects by a single owner-manager. The weaving-shed
with a hundred looms differed from that with five only in
size, and not at all in the complexity of its operations. The
owner could handle it all comfortably – buying, processing and
selling – and there was an abundant supply of cheap labour.
The incentive of threatened hunger took the place of factory
canteens, welfare services and bonus schemes; National Insurance and P.A.Y.E. still lay in the future. Wages were paid in
cash, so administration was simple. These very conditions
contained the seeds of their own abolition, but while they
prevailed the fundamental simplicity of the one-man controller
remained.

Rates of change were also slow. The Victorian mill-owner
would install an extra machine in the confident knowledge that
it would remain as a lifelong asset to be passed on to his sons;
the prudent director of the nineteen-thirties would write off
its value over twenty years; the modern manager is considering
its rapid obsolescence even as he decides to buy.

In science, the day of the gifted amateur was just past its
zenith. Sir Humphrey Davy could isolate sodium with labour
and materials supplied entirely from his own resources; his
pupil Faraday generated the first currents of electricity with a

few simple wires and magnets; Marie Curie wrestled single-handed with her tons of pitchblende in a Parisian backyard.

In such circumstances, the idea of a 'science of management' would have surprised both managers and scientists alike. The notion that so simple and sordid a process as the buying, weaving and selling of cotton could interest a Faraday or a Davy would have seemed ludicrous. The machines themselves, yes, but the *management* – absurd! A few lone voices were raised, Adam Smith and Robert Owen among them, and a few experiments were made, but in the main management remained as a traditional skill, unrecognized as a potential field for scientific investigation.

Now, in the technological explosion of the twentieth century, we see the team predominant. A Henry Ford could no more run his business single-handed in today's conditions than a Madame Curie could build a nuclear reactor unaided. Businesses have grown into organizations of such complexity that the largest of them spread around the planet and spend more each year than many a sovereign state. Specialist managers abound – purchasing officers, financial advisers, market researchers, production controllers, sales administrators, personnel directors – all experts in some branch of management *as such*, distinct from the physics or chemistry or engineering of the processes they control. Management is a study in its own right.

This is the Age of Complexity, when the twelve thousand million cells of the single unaided human brain cannot hope to handle the operations of that mysterious artefact, the Organization. Indeed, there are those who fear that the Organization itself has become the controller of the individual. The paradox is obvious; since no single brain can control the Organization, then it must associate with others to do so – but the association itself is the Organization. The cry of 'Physician, heal thyself!' has become 'Organization, control thyself!'

In the face of this complexity, we are impelled into a search for counterpoising simplicity. Where can we find the means to reduce our problems to manageable size – to strip them of all superfluities so that their essential nature is revealed in stark clarity? How can we then bring them to successful solution?

The answer lies in mathematics, a discipline for handling pure abstractions which yet provides a versatile and objective implement for solving problems in the real world. The clarity and succinctness of its symbols, the precision and unambiguity of its grammar, make it the ideal language in which to describe these problems. Indeed, the skilful rendering of a physical problem into mathematical terms will often provide its general solution without further effort: this will be so if its formulation fits one of the many standard patterns and methods of solution now available for industrial use.

The use of mathematical language in this way is already desirable and will soon become inevitable. Without its help the further growth of business with its attendant complexity of organization will be retarded and perhaps halted. In the science of management, as in other sciences, mathematics has become a 'condition of progress':

There is a condition of progress which, in Britain at least, is of the first importance – the recognition of an adequate scale and quality of mathematical teaching as a necessary condition of effective scientific education. . . . The would-be student, quite early in his progress, comes to a gate through which he must pass if he is to emerge as a fully qualified scientist, armed at all points. On the gate is an inscription in every human tongue: 'MATHEMATICS SPOKEN. ICI ON PARLE MATHÉMATIQUE. HIER SPRICHT MAN MATHEMATIK'.[1]

Some tentative approaches to mathematics in management were made in the first quarter of the twentieth century, but the big advance did not begin until the late nineteen-forties, when two main stimuli arose. The first was the success of mathematical thinking about military operations in the war of 1939–45; the second was the invention of the electronic computer. Military operational research proved the value of mathematics in a special sort of management and gave a broad hint of its potentiality in the industrial field; computers by their speed and relative cheapness raised the upper limit of economically feasible calculation by several orders of magnitude. Indeed, the full power of electronic computation in business has not yet been released, because of the lack of widespread mathematical competence.. These wonderful machines have characteristics quite different from those of the brain, yet all too often they are programmed to reproduce only the most elementary mental processes. Their prodigious capacity for arithmetic is frittered away on simple price extensions and tax calculations. If computers had emotions, then surely frustration would be the first.

There has, of course, been a very real advance in the application of computing machinery and of mathematics in general during the last ten years. To see how this is so, one has only to go back to 1954, when a writer on 'Mathematics in Industry' was able to say:

> The applications of mathematics to industry so far discussed provide justification for the employment of the mathematician as a specialist. Whatever title he or his department is given, his use in enabling industrial problems to be solved on a logical basis is so obvious that the only reason for *his present lack of employment* can be lack of mathematical knowledge by industrialists. This state of affairs should be remedied in time . . . but until it is, the mathematician will remain largely outside the industrial sphere, where his knowledge should be one of those things we cannot afford to be without.[2]

MATHEMATICIANS AND MONEY

Such an apologetic approach already looks old-fashioned in the context of today's scarcity. The demand for industrial mathematicians not only exceeds their present availability but, as Carter and Williams point out:

> the attraction of industry has certainly denuded the school-teaching profession of good scientists and mathematicians, and has threatened the future supply.[3]

The 'attraction' to which they refer is not entirely money, but it must be one of the principal factors. A dedicated teacher will certainly accept a substantially lower salary than his commercial colleagues, balancing other advantages against the difference, but when industry is paying twice as much, it takes a strong-minded idealist to resist the temptation.

There is a conventional hypocrisy amongst scientists which demands that money should never be advanced as the main factor which moves a man into one job rather than another. 'Lack of research facilities' is usually put at the head of the list but this argument is particularly thin in mathematics where so much can be achieved with no more research equipment than a pencil and some paper. Even so unworldly a person as G. H. Hardy ranks, alongside intellectual curiosity and professional pride,

. . . ambition, desire for reputation, and the position, even the power or the money, which it brings. It may be fine to feel, when you have done your work, that you have added to the happiness or alleviated the sufferings of others, but that will not be why you did it. So if a mathematician, or a chemist, or even a physiologist, were to tell me that the driving force in his work had been the desire to benefit humanity, then I should not believe him (nor should I think the better of him if I did). His dominant motives have been those which I have stated, and in which surely, there is nothing of which any decent man need be ashamed.[4]

Why should there be such a big discrepancy between salaries in industry and teaching? Commercial managements will argue that their salary rates are dictated by the inexorable law of supply and demand; does the nation as a whole, the taxpayers and ratepayers, begrudge the money which would provide a counter-attraction towards teaching? Galbraith says of a similar situation in the U.S.A.:

The investment in the refinery is an unmitigated good. It adds to our stock of wealth. It is a categorical achievement. But the training of the scientists and engineers who will run the refinery, improve its economic efficiency, and possibly in the end replace it with something better is not a categorical good. The money so invested is not regarded with approval. On the contrary, it is widely regarded as a burden.[5]

MATHEMATICIANS AS A SCARCE RESOURCE

As a nation, we are squandering our meagre capital of mathematical talent, harvesting the crop without sowing new seed. The wider and more effective use of mathematics in management needs not only an adequate supply of specialist mathematicians but also a higher average level of mathematical education in managers themselves and in the population as a whole.

The Normanbrooke report on British business schools takes account of the second need when it describes two sorts of student, post-graduate and post-experience. In these schools, whose teaching is bound to include the new mathematics of business, the post-experience student will be the developing or mature manager; his purpose in attending the school's ten-week or twenty-week course will be to acquire the knowledge which will enable him to create a suitable climate of opinion for the eager young post-graduates. A very high proportion of this knowledge will be mathematical, and yet another demand for teachers will have been created.

As the Robbins report has said:

... some permanent increase in the proportion of able graduates who become teachers ... will be especially needed in mathematics, where it is also essential that the output of graduates should grow more rapidly than in most other subjects.[6]

We have here a problem of allocating scarce resources, and in any such problem there are two complementary approaches.

(a)   (b)

Fig. 1.1 The isosceles triangle

Pappus' proof : $AB = AC$
$$AC = AB$$
$$B\hat{A}C = C\hat{A}B$$
$$\therefore \quad \triangle ABC \equiv \triangle ACB$$
$$\therefore \quad A\hat{B}C = A\hat{C}B$$

The first, and more obvious, is to create more resources – to attract more people into careers as mathematicians, to increase the number of university chairs, to create departments of applied as well as pure mathematics, to persuade industry to help, to encourage mathematicians to immigrate into Britain and make it less attractive for them to emigrate, and so on.

The second approach is that of the work study practitioner – to make better use of such resources as are available. So much of our present mathematics teaching is not merely wasted, but actually retards the progress of mathematics. This practical, beautiful and easy subject is dragged down to a depressing dullness which begins with learning multiplication tables by rote and continues as a course of systematic memory-stuffing. Norbert Wiener once said that merely repetitive mental work degrades a human being to the level of a machine as surely as purely physical labour turns him into a beast of burden, yet this is exactly what we do in teaching mathematics to our children. We programme them like electronic computers, to produce the appropriate permutations of a limited input when the 'examination' button is pressed. Perhaps we do even worse, suppressing the creative instincts of our children at the same time as researchers try to imitate them with machines. A computer is said to have applied a problem-solving programme to the proposition that the base angles of an isosceles triangle are equal.[7] Instead of the Euclidean proof which proves the

Fig. 1.2 Congruent or not?

two right-angled triangles in Figure 1.1(a) to be congruent, the computer produced, independently, the more elegant but usually untaught Pappus' proof in Figure 1.1(b).

The conventional working must have been taught to millions of children: we may reasonably ask why none of them, apparently, have discovered this simple new proof for themselves. Is it because they have merely been *taught* the proof, and not encouraged to *think* about it? Children have shown so often that their unsophisticated minds are supremely logical. It is more likely that the questioning child has been told firmly that the former proof is 'what the examiners expect'. This rock-crushing argument may well be used to suppress a bright boy who asks how the triangles in Figure 1.2 could be proved congruent by superimposition without the postulate of a third dimension so that one may be turned over. It would have been better to give him Wells's 'Plattner Experiment', Abbott's 'Flatland' and a pair of left- and right-handed quartz crystals to study (Figure 1.3).

(a)   (b)

Fig. 1.3 Quartz crystals

The harassed teacher may well reply with some spirit that he and the pupil together *do* in fact have to satisfy the examiners, and perhaps it is the examiners we ought to examine. There are signs of revolt in the ranks of those most closely associated with the pupils, not only in mathematics but across the whole gamut of science in schools, and ranging from the schoolmaster himself to the Minister for Science:

The school curriculum tends to become a lumber room, to which things are added, but from which they are seldom taken away. . . . There can be no doubt that the revision of science (and mathematics) curricula along modern lines is both highly desirable in itself and would clear the way for all pupils to study science at school in reasonable depth.[8]

The School Mathematics Project and the Midlands Mathematics Experiment are practical expressions of this dissatisfaction, but they are still minority movements largely sustained by the voluntary work of already hard-pressed teachers.

. . . not a single penny comes, or under existing procedures can come, from central government sources even though our work receives, as far as it is possible to judge, the firm approval of the Ministry of Education.[9]

The same report tells us that a similar group in the U.S.A., the School Mathematics Study Group at Stamford University, is supported by the American Government to the tune of over a million dollars a year.

THE SNOBBERY OF PURITY

The second shadow across our teaching of mathematics is the snobbery of purity. Gauss is said to have remarked that if mathematics is the queen of the sciences, then the theory of numbers is, because of its supreme uselessness, the queen of mathematics (although Hardy has questioned the authenticity of this attribution), and

one of the greatest representatives of number theory in the nineteenth century, Kummer, is said to have remarked on one occasion that of all his discoveries he appreciated ideal numbers most because they had not soiled themselves as yet with any practical applications.[10]

The identification of purity with uselessness can be challenged – indeed, Hardy himself does so:

> It is quite natural to suppose that there is a great difference in utility between 'pure' and 'applied' mathematics. This is a delusion: there is a sharp distinction between the two kinds of mathematics ... but it hardly affects their utility.[11]

He goes on to describe useful mathematics as 'dull and elementary'. Such snobbery has a parallel in the arts, where the academic classicist will applaud the study of torture, massacre and rape, provided it is in Latin or Greek (which subjects he has quaintly christened 'humanities'), and argue vigorously that a technical paper in Russian cannot possibly exercise the mind so effectively.

This Olympian detachment from the rough-and-tumble of business may be on the wane, but it dies hard. The motto 'Keep it abstract! Eschew the practical!' can be admirable in research mathematicians, but is not likely to earn much money in industrial management. This is not an attack on research, but only on the arrogant assumption of its universal supremacy. Practical problems can give the mind as much intellectual exercise as abstract ones – indeed they may even give more. The practical investigator must always begin his work in an open system and one of the most important parts of his work is to set boundaries to his problem: he needs the exploratory approach as much as his colleague in research. Granted that the latter may break out of his immediate field of study into a whole countryside of a new branch of mathematics, such achievement is still rare.

NEGATIVE EDUCATION

Whatever the cause may be – shortage of teachers, fossilization of syllabuses or academic snobbery – the average product of the British educational system (and, I suspect, of many others) emerges with inadequate mathematics. (The Russian mathematician Kantorovich has said that Soviet economists had been inspired by a fear of mathematics that left the Soviet Union far behind the United States in the application of mathematics to economic problems, when it could have been a decade ahead.)

Indeed, the achievement of our schools is often negative, in that their students are left not just with indifference to mathematical symbolism, but with a fear of it. Their attitude to even the simplest mathematical equations reflects the primitive tribesman's approach to his ju-ju rather than a civilized curiosity about a rich field of human knowledge. I have little doubt that many potential readers of this book put it down hastily when a flip of its pages revealed some terrifying monster such as

$$ax^2 + bx + c = 0.$$

Hence we find ourselves in the company of astute and intelligent businessmen, men of culture whose conversation may range from the paintings of Kokoschka to the intricacies of international finance, but whose minds have been closed to the stimulating challenge of mathematics. Yet here is a subject which stretches from the metaphysical extremes of pure philosophy to the hard facts of costing on the shop floor – a unique subject in which one may graduate as a Bachelor of Arts or of Science.

The conscientious manager is thus led into a dilemma: on the one hand, he lacks confidence in his ability to understand the language of mathematics; on the other, he may see around him an ever-growing array of monetary benefits from it. The result is bewilderment – in extreme cases, subconscious guilt. The situation is not helped by the disdainful attitude of some mathematicians, who not only regard anyone unfamiliar with their language as a moron, but take little pains to conceal their views.

In the face of such bad manners, I once heard a senior manager of a large company make the comment, 'I have been in this job for twenty-five years, and you tell me I have not been doing it as well as I might. This I am prepared to accept. You go on to say that your knowledge of mathematics alone guarantees that you will do better. This I am inclined to doubt.'

The Franks report[12] speaks of the belief held by many business men that the universities 'are prone to despise applied knowledge and competence. And there is excuse for this in the way some professors talk.'

Nigel Balchin comments on this pharisaical attitude in describing the statistician Till, who

divided people into statisticians, people who know about statistics, and people who didn't. He liked the middle group best. He didn't like real statisticians much because they argued with him, and he thought the people who didn't know any statistics were just animal life.[13]

Till is a fictional character, but many will recognize, if not the man, at least the type. Arrogance of this sort is confined to a minority of the mathematical profession. Nevertheless, it is substantial enough for us to ask what it is based on, at least when directed towards the problems of business. If the mathematician were asked what quality would distinguish his investigation of a practical problem from that of lesser men, he would probably reply, 'Objectivity'. This is a fallacy.

Leaving aside the argument that the pure mathematician's choice of axioms and logical rules may itself introduce an element of subjectivity, let us examine the claim that a mathematical model of an industrial problem is objective. The model will embody certain variables and their functional relationships which purport to represent measurements and rules of behaviour in the real world, but the link between abstract symbolism and reality must be forged subjectively. The operational research worker who says 'Let C be the cost of running out of stock' assumes that there *is* such a cost and that it can be isolated and measured; the statistician who claims that the diameters of steel bars are Normally distributed necessarily implies a small but finite probability that bars of negative diameter could exist. However precise the mathematical treatment may be in itself, as a representation of the real world it must be empirical and approximate. The statistician must modify his claim and say rather that the diameters behave *as if* they obeyed the Normal distribution law – that the model embodied in his quality control chart is adequate rather than absolute. If the cost of running out of stock cannot be measured, then the operations on its symbol may have to be restricted or even dispensed with altogether, by a complete re-formulation of the problem.

NUMERACY

The problem is surely one of communication. If we were not universally literate in the industrial countries, we could not rely on the effectiveness of written messages. The word 'numeracy' was coined in the Crowther report to describe a corresponding familiarity with the language of figures, and the concept is of such overwhelming importance that the appropriate paragraph is quoted here in full:

Literacy has long been important, and its value is as great as ever. Just as by 'literacy', in this context, we mean much more than its dictionary sense of the ability to read and write, so by 'numeracy' we mean more than mere ability to manipulate the rule of three. When we say that a scientist is 'illiterate', we mean that he is not well enough read to be able to communicate effectively with those who have had a literary education. When we say that a historian or a linguist is 'innumerate' we mean that he cannot even begin to understand what scientists and mathematicians are talking about. The aim of a good Sixth Form should be to send out into the world men and women who are both literate and numerate.

It is perhaps possible to distinguish two different aspects of numeracy that should concern the Sixth Former. On the one hand is an understanding of the scientific approach to the study of phenomena—observation, hypothesis, experiment, verification. On the other hand, there is the need in the modern world to think quantitatively, to realize how far our problems are problems of degree even when they appear as problems of kind. Statistical ignorance and statistical fallacies are quite as widespread and quite as dangerous as the logical fallacies which come under the heading of illiteracy. The man who is innumerate is cut off from understanding some of the relatively new ways in which the human mind is now most busily at work. Numeracy has come to be an indispensable tool to the understanding and mastery of all phenomena, and not only of those in the relatively close field of the traditional natural sciences. The way in which we think, marshal our evidence and formulate our arguments in every field today is influenced by techniques first applied in science. The educated man, therefore, needs to be numerate as well as literate. Side by side with this need for understanding a new and essential approach to knowledge, the educated man also requires a general acquaintance with the directions in which science is most rapidly advancing and with the nature of the new knowledge that is being acquired. Neither the understanding of scientific method nor this general scientific knowledge is possible unless a sound foundation has been laid in the main school by thorough mathematical and scientific teaching. However able a boy may be, he cannot reach a Sixth Form level of numeracy except on the foundation of a Fifth Form level; but, if his numeracy has stopped short at the usual Fifth Form level, he is in danger of relapsing into innumeracy. It is now one of the most important tasks of the Sixth Form to ensure that no boy or girl leaves school as innumerate as most have done in the past, and as far too many do even today. The boys' schools at least can no longer be criticized for providing an inadequate proportion of science specialists. The task that boys' no less than girls' schools have little more than begun is that of seeing that the Sixth Former who is not going to be a scientist or a technologist is given enough understanding of the scientific side of human knowledge to be able to hold his or her own in an increasingly scientific and technological world. By whatever means this problem is tackled in the schools, it will make heavy demands on really good teachers. But we believe that it must be done, and that the fruits will amply repay the labour.[14]

Numeracy now vies in importance with literacy as a necessary part of man's mental equipment in an industrial world. It cannot be denied that the general level of numeracy is probably rising, but is it rising fast enough? The gap between need and knowledge may even now be widening, and will certainly grow greater in the future unless more vigorous measures are taken to close it. As a nation we are innumerate.

Although the number of specialist mathematicians in industry needs to be increased, we must also take care that this vanguard does not get too far ahead from the main army of industry, including its managers. If it does, the lines of communication – already stretched too far – may snap entirely. The need for numeracy must be taken as much for granted as that for literacy; the company director who boasts of his mathematical inadequacy is fast becoming an anachronism. The modern politician should be as ashamed of his mathematical deficiencies as he would be of an inability to read.

QUANTITIES AND JUDGEMENTS

On the other hand, the mathematician's deficiency is equally deplorable – the failure to understand the technicalities of the manager's job – especially insofar as it includes *responsibility*. Sir Charles (now Lord) Snow put this point well in speaking of operational research in the Second World War:

> The lesson to the scientists was that the prerequisite of sound military advice is that the giver must convince himself that, if he were responsible for action, he would himself act so. It is a difficult lesson to learn.[15]

Again, the manager is more likely to be aware of the *people* in the problem, who collectively make up the biggest immeasurable factor. Human emotions and aesthetic values cannot be quantified. An industrial problem may be analysed, then, into two main groups of components as shown in Figure 1.4.

Fig. 1.4 Q- and J-factors

The 'Q (for Quantity) Components' box contains everything that can be measured, the 'J (for Judgement) Components' everything else. The 'Research' arrow indicates the attempts to transfer components from J to Q, as in intelligence tests, measurement of mental load, skill-and-effort rating, and merit rating. Leonard Bernstein even tells us that:

> When I was at Harvard, Professor Birkhoff had just published a system of aesthetic *measure* – actually trying to evolve a mathematical system whereby any object of art could be awarded a beauty-rating on a given continuum of aesthetic work.[16]

A pointer to the future may be discerned in the development of new theories of sociology and industrial organization. Rashevsky, speaking of developments in this field of study, says:

> Many significant areas of these disciplines have already been removed by the advances of the past two decades beyond the reach of anyone who does not know mathematics.[17]

There is always, of course, the corresponding reaction shown in Figure 1.4 as tending to undo the effects of research. It ranges from the true scepticism of the scientist to the stubborn resistance exemplified by 'Don't confuse me with facts – my mind is already made up'. At its worst, reaction takes on a spurious appearance of reasonableness, as when the manager says firmly, 'In this business, you simply *can't* forecast', before continuing with his production schedules for the next six months.

Figure 1.4 shows the manager and the mathematician centrally between the two boxes, at what should be their point of contact. The mathematician must concern himself mainly with Q, while remaining aware of the need for the manager's judgement. The manager must be prepared to sacrifice the clutter of routine figure-work and to accept that more of his job may be reducible to mathematical procedures than his pride cares to admit. In doing so, he will free himself for the better exercise of his judgement on more worthy targets. Boole's demolition of a similar argument a century ago, if applied to the broader framework of management rather than to pure logic, is still topical.

> If, through the advancing power of scientific methods, we find that the pursuits on which we were once engaged, afford no longer a sufficiently ample field for intellectual effort, the remedy is, to proceed to higher inquiries, and, in new tracks, to seek for difficulties yet unsubdued. And such is, indeed, the actual law of scientific progress.[18]

COMMUNICATION

Thus we arrive at the purpose of this book: it aims to bring about better communication between the layman – in particular the manager – and the mathematician. If they are to cooperate, there must be a constant interchange of ideas between them, a continuous sharing and examination of the Q and J components. The manager who says, 'Solve this problem for me', is abdicating his responsibility – in any case, his real meaning is often, 'Get out some figures to prove I'm right'. Likewise the mathematician who takes a quick look at the physical realities of the situation, retires to formulate, compute, and produce a 'final' solution with the flourish of a conjurer pulling a rabbit out of a hat, will fail to convince. He must be prepared to explain, as best he can, the concepts and reasoning behind each Q step, checking against the manager's judgement as he goes. The mathematician must remind himself that he is bilingual in English and Number, whereas the manager usually is not. The manager in turn must try to acquire at least a rudimentary vocabulary of the mathematical language and its 'dialects' if he is to use its methods as a practical aid.

The aim of this book is to help build a bridge between the applied mathematician and the everyday world of industry and commerce. Its theme is the use of mathematics to solve problems of physical reality and it is entirely concerned with practical applications: every method described in it has been used by someone, somewhere, to help solve a problem in management. Case studies are used as illustrations, simplified in many cases so that their essential mathematical content emerges uncluttered by the purely local details.

It is not easy to draw a dividing line between management and other industrial applications of mathematics, and the distinction is most easily seen by comparing management applications with others such as process and design studies. Such a comparison is given in Table 1.1: it is neither complete nor representative, but it does serve to show that management is, generally speaking, concerned with the provision and deployment of resources, be they men, machines, or materials. Alternatively, this field of application of mathematics has been defined as 'systems analysis', which considers the thing-being-managed as a system subject to control and operating within an environment with which it interacts. A system may be represented by a model, the analysis of which can lead to conclusions about its counterpart in the real world.

In the chapters which follow, the proportion of plain English to mathematical symbolism is high; the physical equivalent of abstract variables and operators is continually kept in mind. The reader is assumed to have retained the more memorable parts of his earlier education in arithmetic, algebra, and geometry, but a good deal of revisionary work is included. Exercises punctuate the text, and the solution of each is given in full: they will help the reader to assimilate the subject matter step by step.

TABLE 1.1

Technique	Management Applications	Other Industrial Applications
Matrix Algebra	Programme of expansion for a steelworks	Aerodynamic studies in aircraft design
Laplace Transforms	Stock control	Study of electrical circuits
Differential Calculus	Size of a fleet of vehicles	Trajectories of projectiles
Theory of Graphs	Organization structures	Design of printed circuits
Theory of Communication	Study of managerial decisions	Design of transoceanic telephone cables
Statistics	Inventory budgets	Design of atomic piles

It is not intended to be an exhaustive survey, but rather as a shop-window of mathematical technique which may tempt the customer to come in and survey the whole stock more closely.

Chapter 2 deals with project management by network analysis, a technique which needs no more than simple arithmetic and logical thinking, at least in its elementary applications. Chapter 3 introduces algebraic notation for the first time, and shows the wide range of uses of the equation of a straight line. It also introduces the notion of inequalities, which is extended in Chapter 4 to a simple algebraic explanation of linear programming. Chapter 5 retraces the ground covered in Chapter 4, but in geometric terms. The geometric approach will lead to a better understanding among those who are natural visualizers, whereas algebra may have greater appeal to the abstract reasoners[19,20]. Chapter 6 reverts to straightforward arithmetic in describing a particular type of linear programming – the transportation method – which has been applied to problems of distribution.

All these mathematical procedures are illustrated by small examples, but their use in practical situations may call for large amounts of repetitive calculations and hence generate a need for an electronic computer. Chapter 7 underlines this need in describing how the operations of a business may be simulated by a set of logical rules. Accordingly, Chapter 8 introduces the computer by explaining how the manager who wants to use one should go about it, using the network from Chapter 2 as an illustration. Chapter 9 brings us back to algebra with an outline of the uses to which curved lines may be put; finally, Chapter 10 deals briefly with some of the other areas of application of mathematics in management.

The mathematical development has been kept at a fairly elementary level. This has been done not only to make the book understandable, but also because a few relatively simple tools can be usefully applied to a wide variety of problems. Furthermore, greater mathematical sophistication does not always add a new *concept*.

Above all, it is an attempt to break down the widespread fear of mathematics as something beyond the grasp of ordinary men – the idea that only a favoured few possess the right sort of brain to comprehend it. Our mathematical heritage is as great a treasure as our literary one – the fourth centenary of Newton should be as much of a public celebration as that of

Shakespeare. Indeed, one may argue that it is even greater, the language of mathematics being universal.

NOTES AND REFERENCES

1 Hailsham, Lord (now Hogg, Q.), *Science and Politics* (Faber & Faber, 1963), pp. 40–41.

2 Fox, N. W., *Penguin Science News* No. 34 (1954), p. 114 (my italics – A.B.)

3 Carter, C. F. and Williams, B. R., *Science in Industry: Policy for Progress* (O.U.P., 1959), p. 126.

4 Hardy, G. H., *A Mathematician's Apology* (C.U.P., 1940), p. 19.

5 Galbraith, J. K., *The Affluent Society* (Penguin Books, 1967), chap. 19, p. 223.

6 Robbins, *Higher Education*, Appendix Three, (Cmnd. 2154 – III, 1963), Part IV, Section 3, Para. 30.

7 Good, I. J. (ed.), *The Scientist Speculates* (Heinemann, 1962), p. 192.

8 Thwaites, B., and others, *On Teaching Mathematics* (*Southampton Mathematical Conference*) (Pergamon Press, 1961), chap. IV.

9 Thwaites, B., *The School Mathematics Project. Directors' Report 1962–3* (University of Southampton, 1964), p. 9.

10 Uspensky, J. V., and Heaslet, M. A., *Elementary Number Theory* (McGraw-Hill, 1939), 1st edn, p. 20.

11 Hardy, G. H., *A Mathematician's Apology* (C.U.P., 1940), footnote on p. 60.

12 Franks, *British Business Schools* (B.I.M., 1963), para. 17.

13 Balchin, N., *The Small Back Room* (Collins, 1943).

14 Crowther, G., 15–18. *A Report of the Central Advisory Council for Education*, vol. I (Ministry of Education, H.M.S.O., 1963), pp. 270–71.

15 Snow, C. P., *Science and Government* (O.U.P., 1960), p. 29.

16 Bernstein, L., *The Joy of Music* (Weidenfeld & Nicolson, 1954), p. 12.

17 Rubenstein, A. H. and Haberstroh, C., *Some Theories of Organization* (Dorsey Press & Richard Irwin, Illinois, 1960), p. 14.

18 Boole, G., *The Mathematical Analysis of Logic* (Blackwell, 1847), p. 9.

19 Gray Walter, W., *The Living Brain* (Duckworth, 1953), chap. 8.

20 Pearson, E. S., *Journal of the Royal Statistical Society* (1956), Series A, vol. 119, Part II, pp. 125–49.

Similar arguments to those expressed in this chapter may also be found in

Yates, I. and Healy, M. J. R., *Journal of the Royal Statistical Society* (1964), Series A, vol. 127, Part II, pp. 199–210, and Discussion, pp. 221–33.

Plans, Projects and Programmes

> Turn their kind faces from us
> And our projects under construction,
> Look only in one direction,
> Fix their gaze on our completed work.
> Pile-driver, concrete-mixer,
> Crane and pickaxe wait to be used again,
> But how can we repeat this?
>
> W. H. AUDEN, *Nones*

IN this chapter, we shall see how a *project* is subdivided into the individual jobs which contribute to its achievement, and how a study of their logical sequence can give results of immense value to the man in charge of it. By 'project' we mean a scheme to utilize certain resources – usually men, machinery, and materials – in order to reach a defined objective. This may be the completion of a new chemical works or housing estate, the overhaul of a diesel locomotive, the first flight of a new aeroplane, the installation of a better accounting system, or the marketing of a new product. The new technique of 'network analysis' has been successfully applied to all these projects as well as many others; it is a method of allocating priorities to individual jobs, so that a criterion is available for dealing with them in the most effective order. Although the technique is less than ten years old, it has had a great and growing impact on both sides of the Atlantic, and its range of application is spreading.

For the purpose of illustration we shall take the overhaul of an aircraft as our project. The work to be described was actually performed in the hangars of the College of Aeronautics at Cranfield and was a 'Check III' inspection of a D.H. 'Dove' aircraft; the objective to be achieved was 'Inspection completed and aircraft serviceable', and the main resources employed were fitters and inspectors. The whole project may be represented by a single arrow, as in Figure 2.1, which shows the nature of the work and its direction in time. The head of the arrow is the end of the project, which obviously cannot precede its start.

The circles in Figure 2.1, which are called 'nodes', represent the states of the aircraft before and after the inspection. They

Fig. 2.1 Arrow and nodes

are, so to speak, 'snapshots' taken at a moment in time, and therefore the states (of which the nodes are a pictorial representation) are called 'events'.

We can now start to analyse the project, and Figure 2.2 shows the first stages. In (a), the analysis is as simple as

Fig. 2.2 Division of project into jobs

possible: it shows a breakdown into two jobs only. They are drawn as successive arrows because rectification must *of necessity* follow inspection: we cannot put things right until we know where they are wrong. Figure 2.2(b) shows the analysis carried a stage further; again, the jobs follow a logical sequence represented by the chain of nodes and arrows. It is important to note that the sequence is dictated by the logic of the situation rather than by restrictions on resources.

Exercise 2.1

Describe the 'event' which the middle node in Figure 2.2(a) represents.

Exercise 2.2

Suppose that instead of choosing the division in Figure 2.2(a), we had chosen two other jobs

> Inspect and rectify engines
> Inspect and rectify airframe

What is the logical sequence, if any, of these two jobs?

Exercise 2.3

When I take my car to a service station, the attendant first fills the petrol tank and then checks the oil. Is this sequence of jobs logically necessary?

Exercise 2.4

The attendant opens the bonnet before he checks the oil. Is this a logical sequence?

So far, we have considered only simple chains of jobs, but more complicated relationships are possible when concurrent as well as successive jobs are taken into account. Figure 2.3 shows how the network is developed by separating airframe, undercarriage, and engines so that the jobs on these go on at the

Fig. 2.3 Development of network

same time. This network tells us that none of the three inspections can begin until the preparation has been concluded, and that the rectifications cannot be finally checked until all three groups have been dealt with.

Exercise 2.5

Suppose that the single job 'prepare' in Figure 2.3 were separated into the following three jobs:

> Position and jack up aircraft
> Clean undercarriage and remove wheels
> Unpanel and clean engines

Draw a revised network incorporating these modifications.

We can carry the analysis further for each of the three groups. Work on the undercarriage, for instance, is detailed as:

> Clean undercarriage and remove wheels
> Inspect main wheels
> Inspect nose wheel
> Rectify and replace main wheels
> Rectify and replace nose wheel
> Test retraction mechanism
> Rectify retraction mechanism.

The wheels cannot be inspected until they have been removed, and the retraction test cannot be done until they have been replaced. This part of the network will therefore be as shown in Figure 2.4.

Fig. 2.4 Details of work on undercarriage

NUMBERING AND EVENTS

Drawing a network for a project can be a rewarding occupation in itself, because it forces the compiler to think right through the project in detail; the possibility of vital steps being overlooked is much reduced. The full value of a network is not realized, however, until certain calculations have been carried out, and these calculations make it necessary to number the events in a systematic way.

There are several methods of numbering, of which the commonest and most useful is the so-called 'ij' system. Any job has an initial and a final event – the number of the initial event is i and that of the final event, j; the rule for numbering events is that j must be greater than i in every case. The network in Figure 2.4 has been numbered in this way. Any number may be used for the initial event, and 4 has been taken in this case. For a complete network, it is usual to start with either 0 or 1.

Exercise 2.6

Number the network from Exercise 2.5 in accordance with the ij system, beginning with 1.

When a network has been numbered, each job in it can be identified by its ij numbers. In Figure 2.4, 'Test retraction mechanism' is job 8, 9. If the jobs are to be distinguished in this way, each must have a unique pair of numbers.

DUMMIES

The following jobs occur during the overhaul of the undercarriage:

> Test retraction mechanism
> Rectify retraction mechanism
> Recharge emergency system
> General check

Both the rectification and recharging must precede the general check, and neither can begin until after the retraction test. The network for this might therefore be drawn as in Figure 2.5(a). In this 'job 9, 10' could mean either 'rectify' or 'recharge'. In order to avoid ambiguity, a device called a 'dummy activity' is used, as indicated by the dotted arrow in Figure 2.5(b). This is an activity which consumes no resources

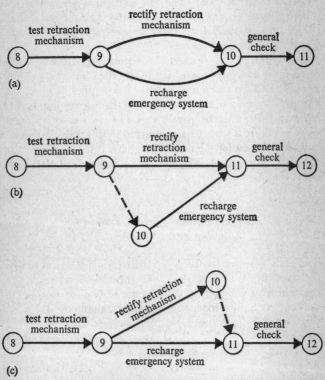

Fig. 2.5 Use of dummies in numbering

and takes no time at all: it merely preserves a logical sequence, and enables us to distinguish the two jobs by their ij numbers. Another possible way of using the dummy is shown in Figure 2.5(c).

Dummies may also be used to preserve a logical sequence even though no numbering problem exists. In the aircraft overhaul, the fire extinguishers may be checked at the same time as the engines, but work on them cannot begin until both engines have been cleaned. The logical sequence can only be drawn with the aid of dummies as shown in Figure 2.6.

Fig. 2.6 Use of dummies to show logical sequence

Dummies whose only purpose is to preserve the numbering system are sometimes called 'identity dummies'. This distinguishes them from so-called 'logical dummies', which play an essential part in the construction of an arrow diagram even though no numbering problem may exist.

Figure 2.6 gives an example. The single job 'Inspect fire extinguishers' cannot be done until both engines have been cleaned. The logical dummy 16, 21 shows that 'Inspect fire extinguishers' must follow the cleaning of the port engine and 20, 21 does the same for the starboard engine. This is the only way of showing the relationship. Otherwise, you may find that incorrect sequences are creeping in, such as the inspection of the starboard engine following the cleaning of the port engine.

Exercise 2.7

Draw a network of the following jobs in attending to a motor car at a service station.

> Driver arrives
> Driver selects brands of oil and petrol
> Fill petrol tank
> Prepare bill
> Receive payment
> Wash windscreen
> Polish windscreen
> Check tyre pressures
> Inflate tyres
> Open bonnet
> Check oil requirement
> Add oil
> Add distilled water to battery
> Fill radiator
> Close bonnet
> Driver departs

Assume that all the jobs must be done. Number the network, using the *i j* rule.

THE COMPLETE NETWORK

Figure 2.7 shows the complete network for the aircraft overhaul, in which many of the features already mentioned may be recognized. A further important point is that the network has only one starting point, event 1, and one end point, event 31: there are no loose ends within the network. This is assured by having a single job (or event) which precedes all the others, as well as one which succeeds them all. There are two such jobs, which are respectively 'Prepare for inspection' and 'General check'.

The network has been numbered by the *i j* rule, but gaps have deliberately been left in the series of numbers used. If it should become necessary to modify the network, extensive renumbering will be avoided if some numbers have been kept in reserve (as will be shown later).

Fig. 2.7 Aircraft overhaul – complete network

The next stage is to estimate the durations of the individual jobs and find out how long the overhaul will take. The practical difficulties of estimation are considerable, but they will not be dwelt on here; we shall assume that discussions between the engineers and work study men have produced a set of values, in hours, as shown in Figure 2.8.

THE CRITICAL PATH

One sequence of jobs in Figure 2.8 has been picked out with heavier arrows than the rest, that is:

Job			
1, 2	Prepare for inspection	1 hour
2, 15	Unpanel engines	3 hours
15, 16	Clean port engine	1 hour
16, 17	Inspect port engine	24 hours
17, 30	Rectify port engine	36 hours
30, 31	General check	1 hour
	Total	66 hours

These jobs make up the *longest path* through the network, and therefore determine the total duration of the project as 66 hours. For this reason, they are called *critical jobs* and the path along which they lie is called the critical path.

Exercise 2.8

Find the path through the network in Figure 2.8 which has the *second longest* duration.

Of the 26 jobs (excluding dummies) in this project, only 6 are critical, in that a delay in completing any one of them would delay the completion of the whole project. On the other hand, there is some latitude in the times for all the other jobs. Finding the critical path enables us to concentrate our attention on a relatively small proportion of the jobs, with a view to shortening the planned project by reducing their durations and subsequently fulfilling the plan by selective control.

FINDING THE CRITICAL PATH

There are only 11 different paths through the network in Figure 2.8, which makes it easy to find the critical path by trial and error. In practice, networks used on large projects may contain hundreds or even thousands of individual jobs, with a correspondingly high number of alternative paths. A systematic and rapid method of finding the critical path is therefore

Fig. 2.8 Aircraft overhaul – critical path

needed. The most common method begins by ascribing an earliest and latest time to each event by working forward from the first to the last events through the successive numbers, and then returning.

At this stage the difference between jobs and events must again be emphasized. A job *endures* in time and we shall refer to its *duration* in hours. The word *time* will be used exclusively for events, which are instantaneous, and to avoid confusion we shall refer to times as *o'clock*. Then job i, j may begin with

Fig. 2.9 Aircraft overhaul – earliest and latest event times

event i at time 3 o'clock, have a duration of 5 hours and finish with event j at 8 o'clock. We shall also preserve simplicity by using times such as '100 o'clock' rather than introducing days.

Let us begin by assuming that the project begins at some time which we shall call zero o'clock. This is then the *earliest event time* for event No. 1, and is shown surrounded by a square in Figure 2.9. Job 1, 2 is completed one hour later, and all the jobs which precede event 2 have now been completed: consequently, its earliest event time is 1 o'clock, also shown in a square. In the same way, the earliest time for event 3 is $1 + 10 = 11$. Continuing along the same path, we should arrive at event 30 at $11 + 28 = 39$ o'clock, if job 3, 30 were the only one preceding it. Obviously, it is not, so we must calculate the event times along the other paths first. This is where the virtues of the ij numbering system become evident; if we calculate the earliest times of the events in their numerical order, then we can be sure that all the jobs preceding an event will have been taken into consideration.

Event 7 is preceded by two jobs, 5, 7 and 6, 7. Since the earliest time for event 5 is at 12 o'clock and the duration of job 5, 7 is 9 hours, the time at which event 7 would be reached is $12 + 9 = 21$ o'clock. On the other hand, event 6 at 11 o'clock plus job 6, 7 at 8 hours gives $11 + 8 = 19$ o'clock for the time at event 7. Which figure should we take as the earliest event time, 21 or 19? Remembering that job 7, 10 cannot begin until *all* the jobs preceding it have been completed, we find that we must take the greater figure, 21 o'clock, as the earliest event time.

Event 30 is preceded by 7 jobs and a dummy (of zero duration) which must also be included, so we have

Preceding Event	Earliest Event Time	Preceding Job	Job Duration	Earliest Finish
3	11	3, 30	28	39
10	22	10, 30	3	25
11	23	11, 30	0	23
13	5	13, 30	1	6
14	20	14, 30	24	44
17	29	17, 30	36	65
22	7	22, 30	11	18
23	25	23, 30	30	55

The greatest figure in the last column is the earliest time for event 30; it is 65 hours and arises from job 17, 30: in this case it also follows that job 17, 30 will be on the critical path.

Finally, at event 31, we find the earliest time to be 66 o'clock, which also tells us that 66 hours is the minimum possible duration for the entire project. This is conventionally taken as the latest finishing time and we work backwards from it to find the latest event times, in much the same way as before. The latest time for event 23, for example, is $65 - 30 = 35$ o'clock. Event 16 is succeeded by two jobs, so one arrives at it through two paths when working backwards: the latest time for event 21 is 52 o'clock, and job 16, 21 has zero duration (as all dummies do) giving $52 - 0 = 52$ o'clock; from event 17 we have $29 - 24 = 5$ o'clock, and this smaller figure gives the latest event time for event 6. It may seem paradoxical to call the *earlier* of the two times the *latest* event time, but the common sense of the matter may be seen when we remember that the project is not to be delayed, and ask what would happen to the overall time if event 16 were not reached until 52 o'clock. The latest event times are shown enclosed in triangles in Figure 2.9.

Exercise 2.9

Event 2 is succeeded by four jobs. Calculate their latest starting times and deduce the earliest time for this event.

Exercise 2.10

The durations of the jobs in Exercise 2.7, in seconds, are

Driver arrives	30
Driver selects brands of oil and petrol	10
Fill petrol tank (average)	120
Prepare bill	45
Receive payment	25
Wash windscreen	20
Polish windscreen	15
Check tyre pressures	80
Inflate tyres	100
Open bonnet	15
Check oil requirement	60
Add oil	25
Add distilled water to battery	30
Fill radiator	50
Close bonnet	5
Driver departs	10

Calculate the earliest and latest event times, and the overall project time (assuming that an unlimited number of men is available).

TOTAL FLOAT

We have already seen that some latitude in event times and job durations may be permissible without delaying the project: this is measured by the 'float' of a job. Take for example job 12, 14 (Figure 2.9). The earliest time for event 12 is at 2 o'clock: if the job were begun then, it would end at $2 + 18 = 20$ o'clock, the earliest finish time. The latest time for event 14 being 41 o'clock, it follows that a delay of up to 21 hours in this job would have no effect upon the overall project time. Conversely, to reach event 14 by the latest time, 41 o'clock, the job need not start until $41 - 18 = 23$ o'clock. This latest start time is 21 hours after its earliest start time, and this 21 hours is called the *total float* of job 12, 14. In other words,

$$\begin{aligned} &\text{Total Float of job } i, j \\ &= \text{Latest time of event } j - \\ &\quad \text{Earliest time of event } i - \\ &\quad \text{Duration of job } i, j \end{aligned} \tag{2.1}$$

Exercise 2.11

Calculate the total floats of the following jobs in Figure 2.9.

14, 30
6, 7
16, 17
20, 23

The float defined by equation (2.1) is called the 'total float'. The reason for this nomenclature is best explained by considering two successive jobs in an unbranched chain. Figure 2.10 reproduces two of the jobs from Figure 2.9, each of which has a total float of 26 hours. It should be obvious that this float can only be used once: it belongs to the path rather than to the individual job. If job 2, 3 were delayed by 26 hours, job 3, 30 would be left with no float at all. Any delay in job 3, 30 would then delay the whole project – in other words, it would have become critical. It follows that all the jobs on the critical path (or paths) have zero float; it is this property which enables us to identify the critical path.

FREE FLOAT

It would be useful to have some type of float which could be allocated to specific jobs rather than to the paths on which they lie. Some systems of analysis apportion the total float according to some arbitrary rule – for example, in proportion to the duration of each job. These 'allocated floats' would then be:

$$\text{For job 2, 3} \qquad \frac{10}{10 + 28} \times 26 = 7 \text{ hours}$$

$$\text{For job 3, 30} \qquad \frac{28}{10 + 28} \times 26 = 19 \text{ hours}$$

$$\text{Total Float} = 26 \text{ hours}$$

The more common practice is to assign float preferentially, as far as possible, to the job at the end of a path. This leads to the concept of 'free float' defined by equation (2.2).

$$\begin{aligned}
&\text{Free Float of job } i, j \\
&= \text{Earliest time of event } j - \\
&\quad \text{Earliest time of event } i - \\
&\quad \text{Duration of job } i, j \qquad (2.2)
\end{aligned}$$

Figure 2.10 shows how this method assigns all the float preferentially to the second job.

Exercise 2.12

Calculate the total and free floats of jobs 21, 22 and 22, 30 in Figure 2.9.

Exercise 2.13

Calculate the total and free floats of the network in Exercises 2.7 and 2.10, and find the critical path through it.

total float of path 2,3,30
= 65 — 1 — 38 = 26

total float of job 2,3
= 37 — 1 — 10 = 26
free float of job 2,3
= 11 — 1 — 10 = 0

total float of job 3,30
= 65 — 11 — 28 = 26
free float of job 3,30
= 65 — 11 — 28 = 26

Fig. 2.10 Total and free floats

THE COMPLETE SCHEDULE

Table 2.1 shows the complete schedule for the aircraft overhaul, summarizing all the calculations described so far. The
jobs have also been sorted into the order of their total float, so
that the critical ones appear at the head of the list. Jobs having
the same float have also been sorted into the order of their
earliest event times. Other systems of sorting are possible – by

TABLE 2.1

Schedule for Aircraft Overhaul

JOB			Dura-tion	JOB TIMES				FLOAT		
				EARLIEST		LATEST				
i	j	Description		Start	End	Start	End	Total	Free	Crit.
1	2	Prepare for Insp.	1	0	1	0	1	0	0	*
2	15	Unpanel Engines	3	1	4	1	4	0	0	*
15	16	Clean Port Engine	1	4	5	4	5	0	0	*
16	17	Inspect Port Engine	24	5	29	5	29	0	0	*

TABLE 2.1—*continued*

| | JOB | | Dura-tion | JOB TIMES | | | | FLOAT | | |
| | | | | EARLIEST | | LATEST | | | | |
i	j	Description		Start	End	Start	End	Total	Free	Crit.
17	30	Rectify Port Engine	36	29	65	29	65	0	0	*
30	31	General Check	1	65	66	65	66	0	0	*
15	20	Clean Starboard Engine	1	4	5	14	15	10	0	S
20	23	Inspect Starboard Engine	20	5	25	15	35	10	0	S
23	30	Rectify Starboard Engine	30	25	55	35	65	10	10	S
2	12	Unpanel for Lubrication etc.	1	1	2	22	23	21	0	
12	14	Check Instruments	18	2	20	23	41	21	0	
14	30	Rectify Instruments	24	20	44	41	65	21	21	
2	3	Inspect Airframe	10	1	11	27	37	26	0	
3	30	Rectify Airframe	28	11	39	37	65	26	26	
2	4	Clean, Remove Wheels	4	1	5	41	45	40	0	
4	5	Inspect Main Wheels	7	5	12	45	52	40	0	
5	7	Rectify Main Wheels	9	12	21	52	61	40	0	
7	10	Test Retraction	1	21	22	61	62	40	0	
10	30	Rectify Retraction	3	22	25	62	65	40	40	
4	6	Inspect Nose Wheel	6	5	11	47	53	42	0	
6	7	Rectify Nose Wheel	8	11	19	53	61	42	2	
10	11	Recharge Emergency System	1	22	23	64	65	42	42	*See Note*
21	22	Inspect Fire Extinguisher	2	5	7	52	54	47	0	
22	30	Rectify Fire Extinguisher	11	7	18	54	65	47	47	
12	13	Lubricate	3	2	5	61	64	59	0	
13	30	Check Lubrication	1	5	6	64	65	59	59	

Note: For the purpose of calculating free float, jobs 10, 11 and 11, 30 are combined. All times are in hours.

event numbers, durations or (with the aid of a suitable code) departments and cost centres.

The critical jobs are indicated by asterisks, and three jobs have also been marked 'S', meaning 'sub-critical'. This rather imprecise term means that their float is relatively low; in this case all jobs with a float of less than 12 hours have been ranked as sub-critical – in other words, as jobs which a relatively short delay could render critical.

REVISING THE PLAN

The plan as it stands calls for 66 hours work to complete the schedule. It can now be used as a basis from which alternative plans may be generated and presented to the manager for decision and action. If we want to speed up the aircraft overhaul,

(a) original sequence

(b) revised sequence

Fig. 2.11 Revision of plan – port engine

Fig. 2.12 Aircraft overhaul – revised network

we should be well advised to direct our attention in the first place towards the critical jobs in Figure 2.9. Take the inspection and rectification of the port engine, for example. The estimates of their durations were made on the assumption that only one man would work on the engine. With two men working, the jobs could be separated into two concurrent sets. Then the old jobs 16, 17 and 17, 30 would become

16, 18	Inspect port engine (A)	6 hours
16, 19	Inspect port engine (B)	18 hours
18, 30	Rectify port engine (A)	24 hours
19, 30	Rectify port engine (B)	12 hours

The original sequence between events 16 and 30 had an overall duration of 60 hours. The new one, shown in Figure 2.11, takes only 30 hours. However, the project itself will not be shortened by the full 30 hours: this is because the sub-critical path 15, 20, 23, 30 becomes the new critical path, losing its 10 hours of float and shortening the overall duration by this amount only.

We can now sub-divide the jobs on the starboard engine in a similar way, and the network becomes as shown in Figure 2.12; the critical jobs are now concerned with the instruments rather than the engines, and the overall duration is reduced to 45 hours. Other variations of the network are possible, but the three versions already discussed suffice to illustrate the factors which affect the manager's decision, as in Figure 2.13. To allocate extra resources will penalize him in some way, either

Fig. 2.13 Aircraft overhaul – resources against duration

by increased direct costs or by delay on some other work, and he must balance these costs against the advantages of a shorter duration.

When this principle is extended to cover the bigger networks which occur in practice, which may involve a dozen or more skilled trades as well as special machinery, the problem of allocating resources becomes very complex. Work in this field is still going on – some successful empirical decision rules have been devised and are being regularly applied. There is also a close relationship between this problem and the family of allocation problems discussed in Chapters 4 and 5: this line of research is being pursued.

Meanwhile, the use of network analysis for controlling large projects is expanding at an explosive rate throughout the world. It is less than a decade since the first successful trials were made, but the essential simplicity of the method has already established it firmly in the toolkit of the modern progressive manager.

2

Solutions to Exercises

Exercise 2.1

'Aircraft inspected but not yet rectified.'

Exercise 2.2

There is no reason why either job should follow the other; they could run concurrently.

Exercise 2.3

No. It is dictated by a restriction on resources, in that there is only one attendant. With two attendants, the petrol and oil could be dealt with simultaneously.

Exercise 2.4

Yes. The job 'check oil' cannot possibly be done before the job 'open bonnet', no matter how many attendants are available.

Exercise 2.5

Exercise 2.6

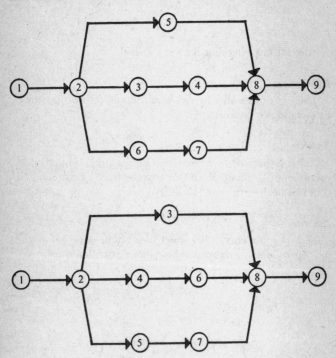

These are two possible solutions under the *i j* system: there are others.

Exercise 2.7

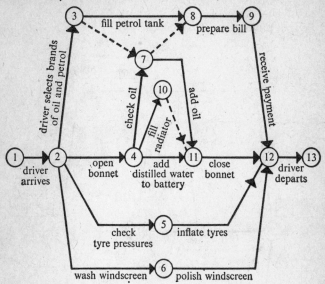

Exercise 2.8

Job 1, 2	1 hour
2, 15	3 hours
15, 20	1 hour
20, 23	20 hours
23, 30	30 hours
30, 31	1 hour
Total	56 hours

Exercise 2.9

Succeeding Event	Latest Event Time	Succeeding Job	Job Duration	Latest Start
15	4	2, 15	3	1
12	23	2, 12	1	22
4	45	2, 4	4	41
3	37	2, 3	10	27

The smallest number in the last column gives the latest time for event 2 as 1 o'clock.

Exercise 2.10

See Figure 2.4.
Overall project time 240 seconds.

Exercise 2.11

Job i, j (hours)	Latest Time, Event j	Earliest Time, Event i	Difference (hours)	Duration (hours)	Total Float (hours)
14, 30	65	20	45	24	21
6, 7	61	11	50	8	42
16, 17	29	5	24	24	0
20, 23	35	5	30	20	10

Exercise 2.12

Job	Total Float (hours)	Free Float (hours)
21, 22	$54 - 5 - 2 = 47$	$7 - 5 - 2 = 0$
22, 30	$65 - 7 - 11 = 47$	$65 - 7 - 11 = 47$

Exercise 2.13

	j	Job Description	Float (seconds) Total	Free	Critical Jobs
1	2	Driver arrives	0	0	*
2	3	Driver selects brands	0	0	*
2	4	Open bonnet	55	0	
2	5	Check tyre pressures	20	0	
2	6	Wash windscreen	165	0	
3	8	Fill petrol tank	0	0	*
4	7	Check oil requirement	55	0	
4	10	Fill radiator	130	0 (see note)	
4	11	Add d.w. to battery	150	55	
5	12	Inflate tyres	20	20	
6	12	Polish windscreen	165	165	
7	11	Add oil	95	0	
8	9	Prepare bill	0	0	*
9	12	Receive payment	0	0	*
11	12	Close bonnet	95	95	
12	13	Driver departs	0	0	*

The critical path is 1, 2, 3, 8, 9, 12, 13. Note that free float which apparently belongs to dummies may often be transferred back to real jobs. Thus the free float of 35 seconds on dummy (10, 11) can be assigned to job (4, 10).

NOTES AND REFERENCES

22 Battersby, A., *Network Analysis for Planning and Scheduling* (Macmillan, 2nd edn, 1967).

23 Lockyer, K., *Critical Path Analysis* (Pitman, 1964).

24 Anon., *DOD & NASA Guide to PERT/COST* (1962), Office of the Secretary of Defense; National Aeronautics and Space Administration, Washington, U.S.A.

3
Graphs and Gradients

How slow Progressive Points protract the Line,
As pendant spiders spin the filmy twine;

FRERE, CANNING *and* ELLIS, *The Loves of the Triangles*

ONE link between the abstract reasoners and the visualizers –
between the algebraists and the geometers, is provided by
algebraic geometry, devised by Descartes in 1650 and variously
known as coordinate geometry and analytical geometry. The
system of rectangular coordinates on which it is based is called
'Cartesian' in honour of the great French philosopher, and
closely resembles the latitude and longitude on a Mercator
projection, as shown in Figure 3.1. In both those systems, the
position of a point on a graph is defined by two coordinates.

Fig. 3.1 Latitude and longitude of Eastbourne and rectangular (or
Cartesian) coordinates of point E

Thus Eastbourne is shown in relation to a reference point at which the 50°N parallel of latitude intersects the Greenwich meridian (0°). Any such reference point is called an *origin*. Eastbourne is 18 minutes east of it and 46 minutes north, as shown by point E in Figure 3.1; we can describe its relation to the origin as E (18, 46). In a more general way, we can call the distance east of the origin 'x' and the distance north of the origin 'y'. For E, $x = 18$ and $y = 46$.

The general expression $P(x, y)$ can denote any point in Figure 3.1, where x is the distance along the horizontal line (called the x-axis) and y is the distance along the vertical line (y-axis).

Exercise 3.1

What are the values of x and y for point P in Figure 3.1?

Exercise 3.2

Draw a graph similar to Figure 3.1 showing the points

$$Q \ (10, 20)$$
$$R \ (20, 10)$$
$$S \ (0, 30)$$
$$T \ (40, 0)$$
$$U \ (25, 25)$$

and label the origin, the x-axis and the y-axis.

One of the great virtues of analytical geometry is that it may be used to illustrate relationships between two variables graphically. Such relationships are called 'algebraic functions'.

Suppose we have a variable y, whose value depends on another variable x: for instance, y (the *dependent* variable) may be the total hiring charge for a lorry and x (the *independent* variable) the number of miles for which it is hired.

This relationship is a particularly simple one and is written algebraically as

$$y = mx \tag{3.1}$$

where m is the mileage rate, say 2 shillings per mile. Note that y is a *total* payment while m is a *rate*. In this case, the value of m does not vary, but is always the same; it is therefore referred to technically as a 'constant', whereas x and y are called 'variables'. We may also write

$$m = \frac{y}{x} \qquad (3.2)$$

Knowing the value of m, we are now able to deduce the value of y corresponding to a particular value of x.

The equation becomes, when $m = 2$,

$$y = 2x \qquad (3.3)$$

and if x is 50 miles, y is 100 shillings. The algebraic equation takes no account of the units which are associated with the numerical values, but merely deals with the values as pure numbers. We must be careful, when dealing with practical situations, to make sure that the units of measurement are the same throughout.

Exercise 3.3

Given $y = 2x$

        (a) If $x = 75$, what is y?
        (b) If $y = 200$, what is x?
        (c) If $x = 0$, what is y?
        (d) Where is the point $P(0, 0)$?

Exercise 3.4

What do we know about the set of points described by the general expression $P(x, 0)$?

(If you find this problem difficult, pick a few values of x at random and plot the corresponding points on a graph.)

Now let us look at the graphical representation of this simple relationship, using two axes at right angles to represent x and y (Figure 3.2). Each pair of values (x, y) is represented by a point on the graph, and all the points lie on a straight line. The function $y = mx$ is called a 'linear function' for this reason, and m is called the 'slope' or 'gradient' of the curve. (Mathematicians use the word 'curve' in a general sense for any line which represents a function, even though it may be a straight line.)

Since the origin of the graph is the point at which both x and y have zero value, the curve of the function $y = mx$ passes

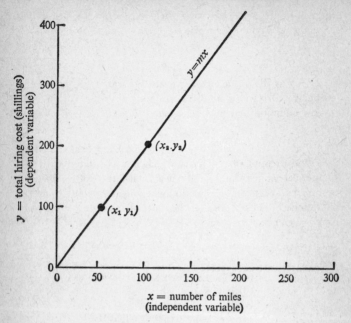

Fig. 3.2 Cost of hiring a lorry

through it. This is not necessarily true of all linear functions: if we were running our own lorry instead of hiring one, the cost would include a fixed weekly sum – call it 'c' – for hire purchase instalments, tax and insurance as well as the mileage rate m. We now have two cases to consider:

    (a) hiring lorries with no fixed cost but a high mileage rate

    (b) owning lorries with a fixed cost but a lower mileage rate.

    The two cases are shown in Figure 3.3. The curve labelled 'Hired lorry' is the same as that in Figure 3.2; the 'Owned lorry' curve is one for which a fixed cost of £10 (200 shillings) is accompanied by a mileage rate of 1 shilling per mile. Its algebraic equation is

$$y = x + 200 \qquad (3.4)$$

which may be written in more general terms as

$$y = mx + c \qquad (3.5)$$

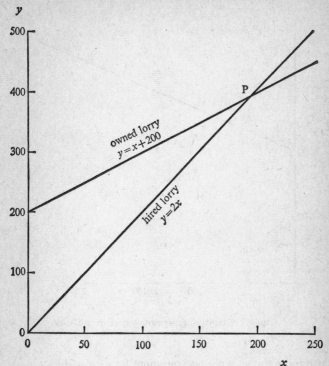

Fig. 3.3 Comparison of two rates of mileage costs

The gradient, m, is 1 shilling per mile and the constant value, c, is 200 shillings in the special case of equation (3.4); c is sometimes called the 'intercept'.

Equation (3.5) is, for all its simplicity, one of the most important and most widely-used in the algebra of modern management. Any straight line you care to draw can be specified by choosing suitable values of m and c, and many business relationships obey a straight-line law.

Try taking a piece of squared paper, drawing an x axis and a y axis on it as in Figures 3.2 and 3.3, and graphing the equations you get by putting various values of m and c into equation (3.5). Use zero and negative values as well as positive ones,

Fig. 3.4 Graphical representation of inequalities

and try to think up physical meanings for the variables x and y as well as the constants m and c which relate them.

Returning to Figure 3.3, it is easy to see that the two curves intersect at the 'break-even' point P where $x = 200$ miles and $y = 400$ shillings. For a weekly mileage below 200, casual hiring will cost less; above this figure hire purchase will be cheaper. This, then, is a geometrical or graphical solution; what is the corresponding algebraic procedure?

Point P is the only combination of x and y which is on both curves and therefore satisfies both equations simultaneously, so

$$y = 2x \tag{3.3}$$
$$y = x + 200 \tag{3.4}$$

It follows that

$$2x = x + 200 \tag{3.6}$$

both sides being equal to y. Subtracting x from both sides of equation (3.6) gives

$$x = 200 \qquad (3.7)$$

Substituting this value in (3.3) gives

$$y = 400 \qquad (3.8)$$

and it is easy to check that equation (3.4) is also satisfied by these values.

P in Figure 3.3 is called the 'break-even point' because the cost y is the same, 400 shillings, whether the lorry is hired or owned.

Exercise 3.5

Rising costs have forced both the hirer and the owner to increase their mileage rates by 20%, but the fixed costs remain unchanged. Does the break-even figure change or not?

Exercise 3.6

The Purchasing Officer of Quaternion Ltd is obtaining quotations for a special spacing piece. Pascal's Pressings have quoted 3d. per item plus a toolmaking cost of £30; the price from Newton and Leibniz Ltd is simply 1/- per item. The Production Planning Department has not yet decided how many parts are required, so the Purchasing Officer calculates a 'break-even' figure. What is it? Find the answer algebraically and illustrate it with a graph.

For the example shown in Figure 3.3 and in the preceding exercise, we used both algebra and geometry to find the break-even point, but the final step of deciding which proposal was cheaper (i.e. which function gave the lower value of y for a given value of x) was by inspection rather than by a formal algebraic procedure. For such a procedure we need to consider inequalities as well as equations.

INEQUALITIES

Inequalities receive scant attention in school textbooks, which is not surprising since mathematicians in general have neglected them until quite recently.

T. Motzkin, in his doctoral thesis on linear inequalities in 1936, was able to cite after diligent search only some thirty references for the period 1900–1936, and about forty-two in all.[25]

The developments of the theory of linear inequalities described in the next two chapters have quickened the interest of mathematicians, and the number of references is now reckoned in thousands. This interest is reflected by the report of the Sub-Committee on Mathematics in the General School Course at the Southampton Mathematical Conference, 1961, which includes the following recommendation:

Inequalities should be considered at the same time as equalities. There is no inherent reason for not doing so. In fact positive advantages are to be gained.[26]

Inequalities may be expressed in several ways, but we shall only be concerned with four of them:

$$y > x \ (y \text{ is greater than } x) \tag{3.9}$$
$$x < y \ (x \text{ is less than } y) \tag{3.10}$$
$$y \geqq x \ (y \text{ is greater than or equal to } x, \text{ i.e. } y \text{ is not less than } x) \tag{3.11}$$
$$x \leqq y \ (x \text{ is less than or equal to } y, \text{ i.e. } x \text{ is not greater than } y) \tag{3.12}$$

The difference between (3.9) and (3.11) is that the latter includes the case $y = x$ while the former does not. In practice, the difference between the two is usually trivial, but must be preserved if ambiguities are to be avoided. For instance, if we specify:

Choose y if $y > x$
Choose x if $y < x$

then the choice for the case $y = x$ is not clearly defined. We must write either

Choose y if $y \geqq x$
Choose x if $y < x$

or

Choose y if $y > x$
Choose x if $y \leqq x$

The inequality signs may be combined with all the more familiar mathematical operators, to give expressions such as

$$y \geqq mx + c \tag{3.13}$$

Inequalities are difficult to manipulate mathematically; this may be overcome by transforming them into equations. In doing so, we make use of a property which many variables possess in industrial problems: they cannot have negative values. The number of items produced in a factory; the percentage of tin in an alloy; the value of last month's sales; the number of cases admitted to a hospital – these are all variables which may at times be zero, but otherwise must have positive values. They are called 'non-negative variables' and are themselves specified by inequalities such as $y \geq 0$.

If $y \geq x$ and both are non-negative, we can write

$$y = x + p, p \geq 0 \qquad (3.14)$$

p is itself a non-negative variable defined as the difference between y and x.

If y is annual income and x is annual expenditure, then equation (3.14) would summarize Mr Micawber's philosophy. 'Annual income twenty pounds, annual expenditure nineteen, nineteen, six, result happiness' with p as a measure of that happiness.

Exercise 3.7

A steel company has six blast furnaces with capacities a, b, c, d, e, and f. Write out the relationship between these capacities and the production y as an inequality, then turn it into an equation with the aid of a non-negative variable z. What is z a measure of?

In many practical situations, the gradient m and the intercept c in equation (3.5) will both be non-negative. If m were negative, the hirer would be paying you to use his lorry.

A useful graphical analogue of an inequality is shown in Figure 3.4. The line $y = mx + c$ divides the total area between the x and y axes into two. The lower portion represents the inequality $y < mx + c$ or, if we consider the line itself to be included, $y \leq mx + c$. In the same way, we can regard the x and y axes as the curves of the equations $x = 0$ and $y = 0$ respectively, dividing the plane in which the graph is drawn

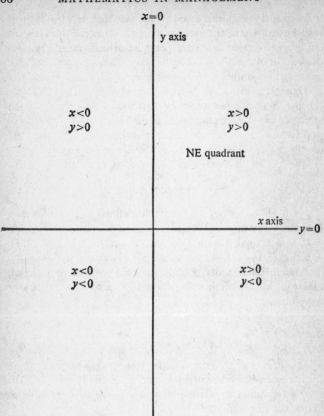

Fig. 3.5 Feasible and non-feasible quadrants

into four quadrants (Figure 3.5). Only the 'north-east' quadrant satisfies the requirement that x and y shall not have negative values.

Exercise 3.8

The Triangle Transport Corporation has now entered the field covered in Figure 3.3, but with a different sort of bid;

they offer a comprehensive service using their own fleet of lorries for a fixed rate of £25 a week. This sum covers not only the use of the lorries, but also their running costs and the driver's wages.

Show this

(a) as a graph

(b) as a linear equation of the form $y = mx + c$ with appropriate values for m and c.

Exercise 3.9

Consider the Triangle Transport bid in competition with the two other offers shown in Figure 3.3. Under what conditions would you accept it?

Exercise 3.10

A supplementary letter from Triangle Transport explains that their offer only applies if the mileage does not exceed 400, i.e. $x \leqq 400$. Show this restriction graphically.

Exercise 3.11

The cost of insuring a 3-litre motor-car comprehensively in the Central London Area is £65 10s. 0d., if its value is £200 or less, plus 10/- for every £100 above this minimum. Express this graphically.

Exercise 3.12

Some investment managers use the variation in the price of a share as a measure of the risk associated with it, and compare it with the yield before deciding whether or not to buy.

The investment manager of Euclid Enterprises takes the highest and lowest values of a share in the previous year, and uses their ratio to measure its riskiness. He also has a maxim, 'Never buy unless the percentage yield is more than three times the price ratio'.

Draw a graph to illustrate this rule, with two areas labelled 'Buy' and 'Do not buy'. Plot the following shares on it:

Company	Yield	High	Low	Ratio
Principia Pty.	5·0%	8/3d	3/9d	2·2
Lagrange Multipliers Ltd	10·0%	2/8d	1/8d	1·6
Axioms Inc.	5·2%	12/9d	7/6d	1·7
Transcendental Corp.	8·3%	44/6d	22/3d	2·0
Vector Space Co.	7·5%	3/6d	1/6d	2·33
Quadratic Corp.	7·7%	27/–d	9/–d	3·0

PLANES AND PAYMENTS

The linear equations and inequalities considered up to now have contained a dependent variable y as a function of a single independent variable x. We now go on to consider a case in which y depends upon two independent variables x and z. Suppose that a chemical plant is producing 160 tons of product in a week, and that the manager decides to increase this figure by means of an incentive bonus scheme. The bonus is to be paid at the rate of one shilling for each ton of production in excess of 160. Then if y is the bonus and x is the production,

$$y = x - 160, \quad x \geqq 160 \qquad (3.15)$$

The chemical engineers point out that increased production may affect the yield unless the plant is carefully controlled. The yield is the ratio of the amount of product obtained to the theoretical amount which would be produced under ideal conditions; at present it stands at 97%. The raw materials are expensive, and a lower yield would increase the cost of the product.

The manager therefore undertakes to apply a penalty of 10 shillings for a fall of 1 point in the yield, and a corresponding bonus for an increase. Such a scheme is called a 'multi-factor incentive', and its equation is

$$y = x - 160 + 10(z - 97),$$
$$y \geqq 0, \qquad x \geqq 160, \qquad z \leqq 100 \qquad (3.16)$$

in which

y is the bonus in shillings
x is the production in tons
z is the yield, as a percentage.

The restriction $y \geqq 0$ is necessary because a negative bonus would be a deduction from the basic rate of pay, which is a privilege permitted only to the Government or a trade union, not to an employer.

Equation (3.16) simplifies to

$$y = x + 10z - 1130 \qquad (3.17)$$

This is still a 'linear function', that is, a straight-line relationship, because it does not contain terms like x^2 or z^3; however, its graph will need to show three variables and will therefore have to be drawn in three dimensions: in other words, it will be a solid, as shown in Figure 3.6.

The vertical axis is y, the bonus, and the two horizontal axes are seen in perspective, sloping upwards from the origin.

Fig. 3.6 Multi-factor bonus scheme

That on the left is the axis corresponding to z, the yield, and the triangle rising vertically is the graph of a relationship between y and z when the production, x, is 160 tons. Similarly, we can see on the right the dependence of the bonus on the production when the yield is 95%. To find the relationship between y and x which applies when the yield is 97% (as in the original single-factor scheme), we must take a cross-section at AA. This graph corresponds to equation (3.15) and is shown in Figure 3.7.

Fig. 3.7 Single-factor bonus scheme
(cross-section AA from Figure 3.6)

The plane surface $BCDEF$ is the graph of equation (3.17) and gives values of y for all combinations of x and z within the ranges shown. The contours drawn across it show its heights above the base, these heights being the appropriate values of y. For instance, the point Q on the base corresponds to the following combination:

$$x \text{ (production)} = 190 \text{ tons}$$
$$z \text{ (yield)} \qquad = 98\%$$

If we draw a line vertically upwards from Q it will cut the y surface at P, on the '$y = 40$' contour and therefore 40 shillings above the base. Check this value by substituting for x and z in equation (3.17).

The shaded area represents combinations of x and z for which y would be negative, were it not for the restriction which does not allow it to fall below zero.

Figure 3.6 can be simplified by presenting it in plan view, as is done in Figure 3.8. The oblique lines again represent

Fig. 3.8 Plan view of Figure 3.6

'bonus contours' and in this form the graph may be used as a ready-reckoner.

Exercise 3.13

The specified upper limit for the main impurity is 0·5%, and the manager wishes to introduce quality as the third factor in his incentive scheme. The rate is agreed with the union as 20 shillings for 0·4%, 40 shillings for 0·3% and so on, with corresponding intermediate values. Batches above the specification limit will be rejected and will not be counted towards the production figure, so no penalty need be applied to the quality factor.

Modify equation (3.17) so as to include this condition, and list the limits of all the variables.

Exercise 3.14

What bonus would be awarded for a week in which 174 tons were produced with a yield of 96·5% and 0·25% of the main impurity?

An interesting contrast between the algebraic and geometric approaches can now be seen, for if the manager wished to bring in yet another factor, the algebraic treatment would merely require the addition of one more term.

The graph of this equation, however, would need to be drawn in four dimensions, which means that we cannot visualize it.

FAMILIES OF CURVES

Suppose we have a linear function of the form

$$2x + 3y = a \tag{3.18}$$

in which x and y are the variables and a is a constant. If we set a to have any selected constant value, then for each value of x there is one, and only one, value of y; y is therefore a function of x, and equation (3.18) may be rewritten as

$$y = -\tfrac{2}{3}x + \tfrac{1}{3}a \tag{3.19}$$

This is a linear function with a gradient of $-\frac{2}{3}$ and an intercept of $+\frac{1}{3}a$. The gradient is independent of the constant a, so all the curves corresponding to equation (3.19) will be parallel. Figure 3.9 shows a family of curves of this type.

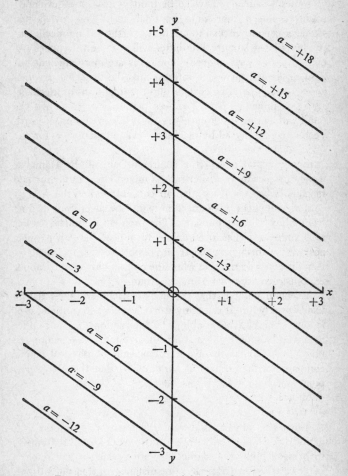

Fig. 3.9 Family of curves of the form $2x + 3y = a$
(The only difference between these straight lines is the value to which the constant a is set.)

The 'opportunity cost' concept of modern economics is derived from such graphs, as is the related idea of an 'indifference curve', although the latter is not usually a straight line. The underlying idea is of a choice between alternatives. For example, a dam may have to be built in an under-developed country, and *a* represents its total cost. The responsible manager can either plan to use heavy earth-moving machinery or cheap local labour. The latter will cost him 3 rupees per cubic yard of earth moved; bulldozers are more efficient but demand capital on which interest must be paid, which when added to the operating costs brings the total cost for mechanical earth-moving up to 2 rupees per cubic yard. Then the family of curves in Figure 3.8 gives the amounts of earth which may be moved by machinery (x) and labour (y) for any given total expenditure a.

In one actual case – the Maithon Dam of the Damodar Valley Project in West Bengal – a mixed effort of labour and machinery was used, with labour concentrated on the difficult corners and edges while machinery did the sheer 'bull-dozing' from which it takes its name. The problem in practice is not so simple as it has been made to appear here: the quick answer 'use machinery wherever possible because it is cheaper' is not necessarily the best when the non-employment of labour is unjustified on social or moral grounds.

A second point is that the use of machinery gives rise to fixed costs before it does any work at all, whereas the cost of labour is completely variable. The International Labour Office is currently sponsoring a study in the State of Bangalore, the object of which is to raise the efficiency of physical labour compared with mechanical handling so that the break-even point (see Figure 3.3) is raised.

Exercise 3.15

A man can move a cubic yard of earth over a given distance in one day, and his daily wage is 3 rupees. It costs 1,000 rupees to bring a bulldozer to the site, after which it can move a cubic yard of earth over the same distance for a cost of 1 rupee.

(a) how big a job (in terms of cubic yards) justifies the use of a bulldozer?

(b) how would this figure be affected if the man's daily output could be increased by 20% with no additional cost?

Exercise 3.16

The cost of hiring a London taxicab was calculated in the following way before the recent fare increases:

(a) For the first three fifths of a mile, or the first seven-and-a-half minutes, or a combination of parts of these: 1s. 9d.

(b) For every additional one fifth of a mile, or two and a half minutes: 3d.

(c) The charge for journeys greater than six miles or lasting for more than one hour is not bound by these rules, but is subject to negotiation.

Draw a graph of these rules as linear functions, showing the total fare in shillings and pence, and using x to denote the duration in minutes and y the distance run, in miles.

Problems of great complexity can often be reduced to sets of linear equations and inequalities, thus making them easier to solve. Such problems are discussed in the next chapter.

3
Solutions to Exercises

Exercise 3.1

$$x = 40, \qquad y = 10$$

Exercise 3.2

Exercise 3.3

(a) $y = 2x = 150$
(b) $x = \frac{1}{2}y = 100$
(c) $y = 2x = \quad 0$
(d) At the origin

Exercise 3.4

All points $P(x, 0)$ lie along the x-axis.

Exercise 3.5

The new values for m in equations (3.3) and (3.4) are respectively 2·4 and 1·2. Then at the break-even point,

$$y = 2 \cdot 4x$$
$$y = 1 \cdot 2x + 200$$

Therefore

$$2 \cdot 4x = 1 \cdot 2x + 200$$
$$1 \cdot 2x = 200$$
$$x = 200/1 \cdot 2 = 167$$

The break-even point has changed. Now find the new value of y.

Exercise 3.6

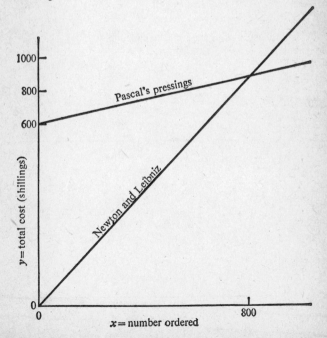

Pascal's Pressings $m = 0.25$ shillings
$c = 600$ shillings
Newton & Leibniz $m = 1$ shilling
$c = 0$

x = number ordered
y = total cost

$\left.\begin{array}{l} y = 0.25x + 600 \\ y = x \end{array}\right\}$ Simultaneously true at the break-even point

from which $x = 800 = y$

Pascal's Pressings are cheaper if the quantity to be ordered is more than 800.

Exercise 3.7

$$y \leqq a + b + c + d + e + f$$
$$y + z = a + b + c + d + e + f$$

z is a measure of spare furnace capacity.

Exercise 3.8

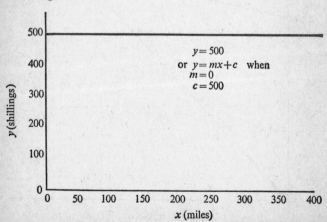

$y = 500$
or $y = mx + c$ when
$m = 0$
$c = 500$

Exercise 3.9

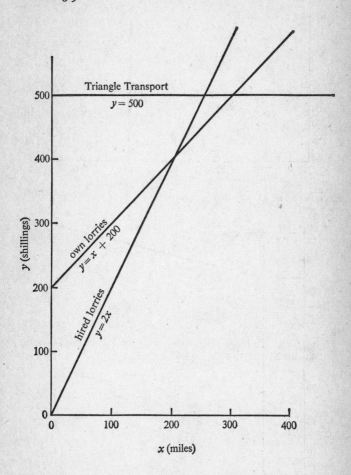

One would accept the Triangle Transport bid only when the weekly mileage was 300 or more.

Exercise 3.10

Exercise 3.11

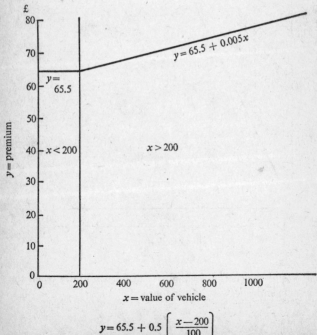

$$y = 65.5 + 0.5 \left[\frac{x - 200}{100} \right]$$
$$= 65.5 + 0.005x$$

Note that, in practice, the premium would go up in steps at intervals of £50 or £100 along the x axis. This is also the case in most managerial problems, and the curves given here and elsewhere are, strictly speaking, approximations.

Exercise 3.12

$$\text{Let } y = \text{yield}$$
$$x = \text{risk}$$
$$\text{Then } y > 3x$$
$$\text{i.e. } y - 3x > 0$$

Sketch the curve $y - 3x = 0$.

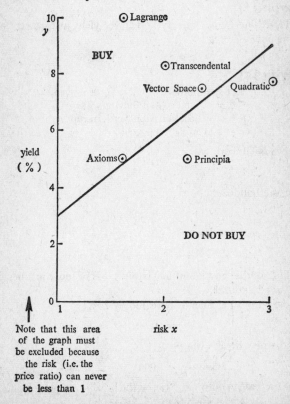

Note that this area of the graph must be excluded because the risk (i.e. the price ratio) can never be less than 1

Exercise 3.13

Let w denote the percentage of the impurity.

$$\begin{aligned} \text{Then } y &= x + 10z - 1130 + 20\,(0{\cdot}5 - w) \\ &= x + 10z - 20w - 1120 \end{aligned}$$

$$y \geqq 0 \qquad\qquad x \geqq 160$$
$$z \leqq 100$$
$$w \geqq 0$$
$$w \leqq 0{\cdot}5$$

Note that w has a negative gradient, indicating that the bonus y increases as the percentage of impurity decreases.

Exercise 3.14

14/–. The higher quality and lower yield just cancel each other out.

Exercise 3.15

Let $x =$ number of cubic yards moved,
$y =$ total cost of moving x,
$m =$ cost per cubic yard, in rupees,
$c =$ initial fixed cost.

For manual work, $m = 3$, $c = 0$.

$$y = 3x$$

For the bulldozer

$$y = x + 1{,}000$$

At the break-even point,

$$3x = x + 1{,}000 \quad \text{so} \quad x = 500$$

It follows that any job of 500 cubic yards or more justifies the use of a bulldozer.

If the output per man is increased by 20%,

$$m \text{ becomes } 3 \div 1{\cdot}2 = 2{\cdot}5$$

At the new break-even point,

$$2{\cdot}5x = x + 1{,}000 \quad \text{so} \quad x = 667$$

The increase in output has raised the break-even point by 33%.

Exercise 3.16

NOTES AND REFERENCES

25 Dantzig, G. B., *Linear Programming and Extensions* (Princeton University Press, 1963), p. 20.
26 Thwaites, B., and others, *On Teaching Mathematics* (Southampton Mathematical Conference) (Pergamon Press, 1961), p. 31.

Opportunity cost and indifference curves are mentioned by (among others)

27 Lipsey, R. G., *An Introduction to Positive Economies* (Weidenfeld & Nicholson, 1963).

28 The use of break-even points is extensively discussed in Knoeppel, C. E., and Seybold, E. G., *Managing for Profit* (McGraw-Hill, 1937).

4
Allocation by Algebra

'The sum of all the parts of Such –
Of each laboratory scene –
Is Such?' While Science means this much
And means no more, why, let it mean!

ROBERT GRAVES, *Synthetic Such*

INTRODUCTION

Managers are as diverse in their interests as the companies they work in, but they all have one major problem in common: scarcity of resources. Labour, machinery, buildings, space, and labour are never available in unlimited quantities, and all management plans have to be made within the restrictions which they impose. The prudent allocation of resources is always a problem, but a powerful weapon for attacking it has been developed by mathematicians. It is known by the generic description of 'mathematical programming', but we shall consider here only the simplest and most widely-used member of the genus, linear programming. This is no mere academic curiosity, but a sound practical means of producing workable plans and increased profits. Transporting coal to power stations or gasworks, allocating cash to local branches, formulating foods and drawing up a maintenance schedule: these are all areas in which linear programming is at work today. Other examples are quoted later.

One could hardly expect the busy manager to slog through the calculations described in this chapter as part of his daily routine, but he ought to go through them for himself at least once. In doing so, he will learn a good deal about the limitations of the method as well as its potentialities, and be able to assess its appropriateness to his own circumstances. Furthermore, he will be able to set out his problem, possibly with some expert help, in a standardized form, and then delegate the routine calculations to either a human computer or an electronic one.

In the Glacier Metal case (described briefly at the end of Chapter 5), a girl with a desk calculating machine was able, after a week's training, to compute a re-melting plan in three hours. The plan had previously been drawn up by a research investigator, whose time was more costly, by rule of thumb. A comparison of the two methods showed that the girl got better answers.

Once the manager has acquired confidence in this remarkably versatile technique, he can afford to forget how he originally did the calculations and concentrate on the more interesting parts of the job – defining the problem and interpreting its solution in terms of practical decisions.

The descriptions which follow may at times make fairly heavy demands on the rusty non-mathematician; nevertheless, they consist entirely in juggling with simple equations as was done in the last chapter. Since one very common application of linear programming is to production control, the elementary case in this chapter is taken from that field of management.

A PRODUCTION PLANNING PROBLEM

The Fermat Furniture Company manufactures tables, chairs, desks, and bookcases. A table requires 5 feet of softwood and 2 feet of hardwood, and takes up 3 man-hours. These requirements and those for the other types are summarized in the table below:

Item	Softwood (ft)	Hardwood (ft)	Man-hours
Table	5	2	3
Chair	1	3	2
Desk	9	4	5
Bookcase	12	1	10

1,500 feet of softwood and 1,000 feet of hardwood are available. The factory employs 10 men, each of whom works 8 hours a day. (The man-hours given in the table above include suitable allowances for rest-periods, etc. Overtime is not permitted.) Production is planned over a 10-day period according to sales requirements.

The Sales Manager has asked for at least 40 tables, 130 chairs, and 30 desks, and says he can sell any production in excess of these figures. There is little demand for bookcases, so there is no minimum requirement and the Sales Manager does not think he could accept more than 10 for sale.

The question is how the production should be planned, and the first step in solving it is a simple one. We accept the Sales Manager's assessment of the market and assume that his minimum requirements will first be met in full. They will use some of the available resources as shown in the following table:

Item	No.	Softwood (ft)	Hardwood (ft)	Man-hours
Table	40	200	80	120
Chair	130	130	390	260
Desk	30	270	120	150
Bookcase	0	0	0	0
Sub-totals		600	590	530
Total Resources		1,500	1,000	800
Nett Resources Remaining		900	410	270

We are left with the problem of allocating the remaining productive resources – softwood, hardwood, and man-hours – to tables, chairs, desks, or bookcases, singly or in combination. Which of the many possible answers should we choose? In order to find an answer we must have some *criterion* of selection.

The simplest criterion of all is that of *feasibility* – that is to say, of finding a solution which lies within the limits of the resources available; in our example, we might decide to make 10 bookcases and 80 chairs above the minimum requirements.

Exercise 4.1

Confirm that 10 bookcases and 80 chairs constitute a feasible plan.

The criterion of *feasibility* is a crude one: why then is it so widely used? Simply because real-life problems are so much more complex than our over-simplified example that merely to achieve feasibility is a considerable feat of mental agility. As Doctor Johnson said of 'a dog's walking on his hind legs. It is not done well; but you are surprised to find it done at all'.

A more refined criterion which is also used extensively is minimum idle time. Since the plant presumably makes a profit when it is running and merely incurs costs when it is idle, the plan which most utilizes the productive resources will, one assumes, be the best. In the Fermat Furniture Company, the only measure of 'plant capacity' is the number of man-hours worked: the feasible solution we have already proposed leaves 10 idle hours which we might allocate to, say, 2 desks. Although minimum idle time can give an improvement on mere feasibility, its employment as a criterion can sometimes give fallacious results, as will be shown later.

The most modern method is to use a financial criterion, usually *minimum cost* or *maximum profit*, the latter being preferable. To this end we need to know costs and prices which for Fermat Furniture are:

Softwood costs 2/– per foot.
Hardwood costs 5/– per foot.

The labour cost, including machine costs and all direct costs (e.g. electricity, lubricants) but excluding overheads, is 10/– per hour.

The prices at which the products are offered to the trade are:

Table	£3	2	0
Chair	£2	2	0
Desk	£5	3	0
Bookcase	£6	19	0

Calculating the profit on each item is a straightforward procedure:

Item	Soft-wood 2/– ft	Cost	Hard-wood 5/– ft	Cost	Man-hours 10/– Hours	Cost	Total Cost	Shillings Sell-ing Price	Gross Profit
Table	5	10	2	10	3	30	50	62	12
Chair	1	2	3	15	2	20	37	42	5
Desk	9	18	4	20	5	50	88	103	15
Book-case	12	24	1	5	10	100	129	139	10

The gross profit on our feasible solution would be

10 bookcases:	100 shillings
80 chairs:	400 shillings
2 desks:	30 shillings
Total:	530 shillings

(plus, of course, a profit of 1,580 shillings made by manu-facturing and selling the minimum requirements, which from now on will be taken for granted).

It is not difficult to select better plans now that we know about costs, as the two exercises which follow will show.

Exercise 4.2

(a) Which item shows the greatest profit per unit manu-factured?
(b) How many can we make?
(c) What would be the profit?
(d) What stops us from making any more?

Exercise 4.3

(a) Which item shows the greatest profit per man-hour?
(b) How many can we make?
(c) What would be the profit?
(d) What stops us from making any more?

In this small example, it is not difficult to work out that the most profitable plan is to make 90 tables, but the fact that taking profit-per-man-hour leads us to the best solution in this example should not be taken to mean that this is always so.

ALGEBRAIC STATEMENT OF THE PROBLEM

Let us now set out in formal algebraic terms the second part of the problem – that is, of employing the resources remaining after the minimum requirements have been satisfied.

> Let t = number of tables made,
> c = number of chairs made,
> d = number of desks made,
> b = number of bookcases made.

The amount of softwood used in making t, c, d and b, will be expressed by the linear function:

$$5t + c + 9d + 12b$$

Since the amount used cannot exceed what is available, i.e. 900 ft, we have the inequality:

$$5t + c + 9d + 12b \leqq 900 \tag{4.1}$$

which can be transformed into an equation by adding a non-negative variable p, (see equation 3.14):

$$5t + c + 9d + 12b + p = 900 \tag{4.2}$$

p represents the amount of softwood available for use but not taken up, and we must remember that t, c, d and b are also non-negative variables.

Exercise 4.4

Write down the equation corresponding to (4.2) but which relates to man-hours instead of softwood.

What does the additional variable represent?

Exercise 4.5

Write down an equation which expresses algebraically the limit on the number of bookcases which can be sold.

Exercise 4.6

Write down an equation for the profit P which is a linear function of t, c, d and b.

Proceeding in this way, we arrive at a set of simultaneous linear equations defining the restrictions within which we must work. They are:

Softwood: $5t + c + 9d + 12b + p = 900$ (4.2)
Hardwood: $2t + 3c + 4d + b + q = 410$ (4.3)
Man-hours: $3t + 2c + 5d + 10b + r = 270$ (4.4)
Market: $b + s = 10$ (4.5)

By covering up the labels on the left-hand side, we can see that the 'man-hours' equation does not differ in form from the two 'wood' equations, implying that there is no reason for treating man-hours as having any special quality. Why should we not use, say 'minimum idle softwood' as a guide to the best solution?

Before answering this question, we must consider the mathematical problem of equations (4.2) to (4.5). There are only four of them, but they contain eight unknown variables. We cannot therefore 'solve' them in the conventional sense of obtaining a single value for each of the variables: apparently we have reached a dead end.

The way out is indicated by the profit equation

$$P = 12t + 5c + 15d + 10b \qquad (4.6)$$

because P is a quantity we want to make as large as possible. We need to find a set of values for the eight variables which will simultaneously satisfy the restrictions imposed by equations (4.2) to (4.5) and maximize the profit P: this will give us the unique solution we are seeking.

METHOD OF SOLUTION

It is convenient to transpose the equations so that the problem is stated in the following form:

$$p = 900 - 5t - c - 9d - 12b \qquad (4.7)$$
$$q = 410 - 2t - 3c - 4d - b \qquad (4.8)$$
$$r = 270 - 3t - 2c - 5d - 10b \qquad (4.9)$$
$$s = 10 - b \qquad (4.10)$$

Maximize $\quad P = \qquad 12t + 5c + 15d + 10b \qquad (4.6)$

The procedure for finding maximum profit starts from any feasible solution: we could take one of those already described, but the calculation in this case is easier if we take the simplest possible solution, which is to do nothing. Then t, c, d and b are all zero; $p = 900$ because all the softwood is available but not used; similarly $q = 410$, $r = 270$, $s = 10$ and of course there is no profit, so $P = 0$.

We go on to consider the various possibilities for increasing P. All the terms on the right-hand side of equation (4.6) have positive signs in front of them, so to increase any of t, c, d or b will automatically increase P. None of them may be increased indefinitely, however, as may be seen by considering the first variable, t. From equation (4.7), if c, d and b are held at zero, we have

$$p = 900 - 5t.$$

p becomes zero when t reaches 180, so t cannot be increased beyond this figure if p is to remain non-negative. In real terms, if our 900 feet of softwood are used exclusively for making tables, then at 5 feet per table we have enough to make 180 tables with none left over ($p = 0$). The hardwood equation (4.8) restricts t to $\frac{410}{2} = 205$; man-hours restrict it to $\frac{270}{3} = 90$, but no restriction is imposed by the market for bookcases, equation (4.10).

The operative restriction will be the one which gives the lowest value, $t = 90$; it is equation (4.9). What we may do, therefore, is to increase t up to the point at which r becomes zero – in real terms, to use up all the available man-hours by making 90 tables. We have now taken a step towards improved profit. At this stage (and also in any subsequent steps) we have increased one variable, t, *from* zero and reduced another, r, *to* zero. The particular method of solution we are using here demands that all variables which become zero must be moved to the right-hand side of the equations and all the non-zero ones must be on the left; r therefore has to be moved across to the right-hand side, where it joins the other zero values. We transpose equation (4.9) into:

$$3t = 270 - 2c - 5d - 10b - r$$
$$\therefore \quad t = 90 - \tfrac{2}{3}c - \tfrac{5}{3}d - \tfrac{10}{3}b - \tfrac{1}{3}r \qquad (4.13)$$

We also remove t from the right-hand side of the other equations by substituting equation (4.13). In doing so, we introduce a term in r. Thus:

$$p = 900 - c - 9d - 12b - 450 + \tfrac{10}{3}c + \tfrac{25}{3}d + \tfrac{50}{3}b + \tfrac{5}{3}r$$
$$= 450 + \tfrac{7}{3}c - \tfrac{2}{3}d + \tfrac{14}{3}b + \tfrac{5}{3}r \tag{4.11}$$

Exercise 4.7

Find the new expression for the profit, P, by substituting equation (4.13) into equation (4.6).

The final result is the following group of equations:

$$p = 450 + \tfrac{7}{3}c - \tfrac{2}{3}d + \tfrac{14}{3}b + \tfrac{5}{3}r \tag{4.11}$$
$$q = 230 - \tfrac{5}{3}c - \tfrac{2}{3}d + \tfrac{17}{3}b + \tfrac{2}{3}r \tag{4.12}$$
$$t = 90 - \tfrac{2}{3}c - \tfrac{5}{3}d - \tfrac{10}{3}b - \tfrac{1}{3}r \tag{4.13}$$
$$s = 10 \qquad\qquad\quad - b \tag{4.14}$$
$$P = 1080 - 3c - 5d - 30b - 4r \tag{4.15}$$

Look first of all at the new expression for P: whereas all the terms on the right-hand side of equation (4.6) had positive values, all those in equation (4.15) have negative signs; that is to say, any increase in c, d, b or r will *decrease* P, and since negative values are not permitted, no further increase in P is possible. The value of 1080, obtained by putting c, d, b and r equal to zero, is therefore the maximum value of P. The set of equations (4.11) to (4.15) is called the *optimum* solution; 'optimum' is a general expression signifying a maximum or minimum, whichever is appropriate. Here it means maximum, but for a minimum-cost criterion it would denote the final minimum value.

Since one of the computational rules was that *all* the variables on the right-hand side of any equation must be zero, it follows that c, d, b and r are all zero. Substituting these zero values in equations (4.11) to (4.15) gives the values of p, q, t, s and P as being equal to 450, 230, 90, 10 and 1080 respectively. Every one of these values has some practical significance as follows:

$$\left.\begin{array}{l} c = 0 \\ d = 0 \\ b = 0 \end{array}\right\}$$ No chairs, desks or bookcases are to be made.

$r = 0$ No man-hours will remain unused.

$p = 450$ ⎱   These are the amounts of softwood and hardwood
$q = 230$ ⎰   respectively which are not used.

$t = 90$ Gives the number of tables to be made.

$s = 10$ None of the market for bookcases will be taken up.

SELECTING A DIFFERENT ROUTE

Supposing we had not picked on t as the variable to be increased – what then? An alternative candidate is d, because it
has the largest coefficient in equation (4.6). The restrictions on
increasing d are:

From equation (4.7) $\frac{900}{9} = 100$
         (4.8) $\frac{410}{4} = 102\cdot5$
         (4.9) $\frac{270}{5} = 54$
         (4.10)   None

Man-hours are, as before, the operative restriction, so we
again transpose equation (4.9), but this time bringing d over
to the left-hand side:

$$d = 54 - \tfrac{3}{5}t - \tfrac{2}{5}c - 2b - \tfrac{1}{5}r \qquad (4.18)$$

Substituting (4.18) in the remaining equations gives:

$$p = 414 + \tfrac{2}{5}t + \tfrac{13}{5}c + 6b + \tfrac{9}{5}r \qquad (4.16)$$
$$q = 194 + \tfrac{2}{5}t - \tfrac{7}{5}c + 7b + \tfrac{4}{5}r \qquad (4.17)$$
$$d = \ \ 54 - \tfrac{3}{5}t - \tfrac{2}{5}c - 2b - \tfrac{1}{5}r \qquad (4.18)$$
$$s = \ \ 10 \qquad\qquad - b \qquad\qquad (4.19)$$
$$P = 810 + 3t - \ \ c - 20b - 3r \qquad (4.20)$$

The profit has again increased, but to a lower figure than
before, and equation (4.20) still has a variable term with a
positive sign, namely, $+3t$. We know from this that P can
be made even greater by increasing t, and the only equation
restricting the increase is (4.18) which gives $t = 54 \div \tfrac{3}{5} = 90$
as the point beyond which d would become negative. Equation
(4.18) is therefore the one we must transpose in order to bring
the variable d, with its new value of zero, to the right-hand
side:

$$t = 90 - \tfrac{2}{3}c - \tfrac{5}{3}d - \tfrac{10}{3}b - \tfrac{1}{3}r$$

which is identical with equation (4.13) and substitution into

(4.16), (4.17), (4.19) and (4.20) gives the optimum solution shown in (4.11) to (4.15).

Had we started with c instead of d, we should first have arrived at a plan to make 135 chairs and a profit equation as follows:

$$P = 675 + \tfrac{9}{2}t + \tfrac{5}{2}d - 15b - \tfrac{5}{2}r \qquad (4.21)$$

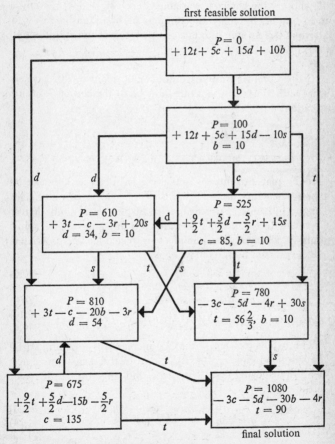

first feasible solution

$$P = 0$$
$$+ 12t + 5c + 15d + 10b$$

b

$$P = 100$$
$$+ 12t + 5c + 15d - 10s$$
$$b = 10$$

d d c t

$$P = 610$$
$$+ 3t - c - 3r + 20s$$
$$d = 34,\ b = 10$$

d

$$P = 525$$
$$+ \tfrac{9}{2}t + \tfrac{5}{2}d - \tfrac{5}{2}r + 15s$$
$$c = 85,\ b = 10$$

s t s t

$$P = 810$$
$$+ 3t - c - 20b - 3r$$
$$d = 54$$

$$P = 780$$
$$- 3c - 5d - 4r + 30s$$
$$t = 56\tfrac{2}{3},\ b = 10$$

d t s

$$P = 675$$
$$+ \tfrac{9}{2}t + \tfrac{5}{2}d - 15b - \tfrac{5}{2}r$$
$$c = 135$$

t

$$P = 1080$$
$$- 3c - 5d - 30b - 4r$$
$$t = 90$$

final solution

Fig. 4.1 Summary of all possible ways of arriving at the solution of equations (4.6) to (4.10)

Here there are two positive terms in the equation: increasing t would take us straight to the optimum solution, whereas increasing d would take us there by the indirect route through equations (4.16) to (4.20).

No matter which variable we choose in equation (4.6), the routine just described will lead us to the optimum solution, as is shown in Figure 4.1. As long as variables with positive signs are chosen, the choice of variable at each stage does not affect the solution, but only the number of 'iterations' needed to arrive at it. (An iteration is a complete set of transpositions.)

Exercise 4.8

If the variables transposed are b, c, d, s and t in that order, what is the form of the profit function at the end of the third iteration?

TWO OPERATIVE RESTRICTIONS

The Fermat Furniture Company have decided to make 90 tables when they are told that the timber merchant no longer has the full amount of softwood available: he can only deliver up to 980 feet. Since 600 feet are used for satisfying the minimum requirements, only 380 feet are available. The problem is now expressed by the following equations:

$$p = 380 - 5t - c - 9d - 12b \qquad (4.22)$$
$$q = 410 - 2t - 3c - 4d - b \qquad (4.8)$$
$$r = 270 - 3t - 2c - 5d - 10b \qquad (4.9)$$
$$s = 10 \qquad\qquad\qquad - b \qquad (4.10)$$
$$P = \qquad 12t + 5c + 15d + 10b \qquad (4.6)$$

The extent to which t may be increased is now limited by the softwood equation (4.22) instead of the man-hours equation. Transposing t and p in (4.22) and substituting the result in the other equations gives:

$$t = 76 - \tfrac{1}{5}c - \tfrac{9}{5}d - \tfrac{12}{5}b - \tfrac{1}{5}p \qquad (4.23)$$
$$q = 258 - \tfrac{13}{5}c - \tfrac{2}{5}d + \tfrac{19}{5}b + \tfrac{2}{5}p \qquad (4.24)$$
$$r = 42 - \tfrac{7}{5}c + \tfrac{2}{5}d - \tfrac{14}{5}b + \tfrac{3}{5}p \qquad (4.25)$$
$$s = 10 \qquad\qquad - b \qquad (4.26)$$
$$P = 912 + \tfrac{13}{5}c - \tfrac{33}{5}d - \tfrac{94}{5}b - \tfrac{12}{5}p \qquad (4.27)$$

and a further iteration on c gives the final solution:

$$t = 70 - \tfrac{13}{7}d - 2b - \tfrac{2}{7}p + \tfrac{1}{7}r \qquad (4.28)$$
$$q = 180 - \tfrac{5}{7}d + 9b - \tfrac{5}{7}p + \tfrac{13}{7}r \qquad (4.29)$$
$$c = 30 + \tfrac{2}{7}d - 2b + \tfrac{3}{7}p - \tfrac{5}{7}r \qquad (4.30)$$
$$s = 10 \phantom{+ \tfrac{2}{7}d} - b \qquad\qquad\qquad (4.31)$$
$$P = 990 - \tfrac{41}{7}d - 24b - \tfrac{9}{7}p - \tfrac{13}{7}r \qquad (4.32)$$

Exercise 4.9

Remembering that all variables on the right-hand side are put equal to zero, write out the interpretation of equations (4.28) to (4.32) as was done on page 94.

It is noteworthy that *two* factors – softwood and man-hours – are now restricting the profit in the final solution, and the plan calls for *two* products to be manufactured. Finding the solution by linear programming required no more effort than when one restriction was operative, whereas obtaining a two-product solution by trial and error would have been a long and tedious process.

THE VALUE OF OVERTIME

Knowing that man-hours are one of the operative restrictions on profit, the management of the Fermat Furniture Company decides to re-examine its policy on overtime. What would be the effect of allowing a single extra hour of overtime to be worked? First, the original equation for man-hours, (4.4), would become:

$$3t + 2c + 5d + 10b + r = 271. \qquad (4.33)$$

This equation could be transposed and the whole calculation worked through again: there is, however, a quicker way.

Suppose we define a new variable u, such that

$$u = r - 1.$$

Then:

$$3t + 2c + 5d + 10b + u = 270.$$

which has exactly the same form as the original equation (4.4). In other words, increasing the number of available man-hours by 1 is the same as letting r, previously a non-negative variable, decrease as far as -1 instead of to 0.

In the solution equations (4.28) to (4.32), if r becomes -1, P increases to $990 - (\frac{13}{7} \times -1) = 991\frac{6}{7}$. It follows that working overtime will increase the profit provided that the premium paid for overtime does not exceed $\frac{13}{7}$ shillings – about 1s. 10d. – per hour: this is therefore a break-even figure, above which overtime is not profitable.

Exercise 4.10

If more softwood could be obtained from another supplier at a higher price, up to how much extra should we be prepared to pay for it?

Exercise 4.11

What is the corresponding figure for hardwood?

The coefficients of the variables on the right-hand side of equation (4.32) are called 'incremental values', and it is interesting to examine the others. The coefficient of d, for instance, is $-\frac{41}{7}$: what can we deduce from it?

PROFIT ON DESKS

Allowing d to become zero means that no desks other than the minimum requirements are to be made. For d to become negative, the Sales Manager's original estimate must be questioned. Making one desk less ($d = -1$) would cause the profit to increase by $\frac{41}{7}$ shillings (5s. 10d.) This result appears paradoxical, until we look at the results of putting $d = -1$ in the other equations. Because of integral restrictions – we cannot make fractions of items of furniture – it is more sensible to put $d = -7$, giving

$$
\begin{aligned}
t &= 70 + 13 = 83 \\
q &= 180 + 8 = 188 \\
c &= 30 - 2 = 28 \\
s &= 10 \\
P &= 990 + 41 = 1031
\end{aligned}
$$

The extra profit is earned by making 7 desks less, simultaneously reducing the number of chairs made by 2 and using the softwood and man-hours so released for the manufacture of 13 additional tables.

Exercise 4.12

Verify that the softwood and man-hours released are enough to make the extra tables.

THE PRICE OF BOOKCASES

If one bookcase less were made, the profit would increase by 24 shillings, but we cannot do this because there are no minimum requirements to be dipped into, as there were for desks. There is, however, a clear implication that the price of bookcases is too low in relation to the other items: if it were increased by 25 shillings, equation (4.32) would become

$$P = 990 - \tfrac{4\frac{1}{7}}{}d + b - \tfrac{9}{7}p - \tfrac{1\frac{3}{7}}{}r$$

and a further iteration would be needed to get the final solution:

$$
\begin{aligned}
t &= & 50 - \tfrac{1\frac{3}{7}}{}d & - \tfrac{2}{7}p + \tfrac{1}{7}r + 2s & (4.34) \\
q &= & 270 - \tfrac{8}{7}d & - {\scriptstyle 7}p + \tfrac{1\frac{3}{7}}{}r - 9s & (4.35) \\
c &= & 10 + \tfrac{2}{7}d & + \tfrac{3}{7}p - \tfrac{5}{7}r + 2s & (4.36) \\
b &= & 10 & - s & (4.37) \\
P &= & 1000 - \tfrac{4\frac{1}{7}}{}d & - \tfrac{9}{7}p - \tfrac{1\frac{3}{7}}{}r - s & (4.38)
\end{aligned}
$$

20 tables and 20 chairs have been sacrificed to make 10 bookcases for an extra profit of 10 shillings. Incidentally, the term in s in equation (4.38) shows that it would now pay us to spend up to 1 shilling, per bookcase sold, on expanding the market for bookcases.

It is not difficult to show that this result is consistent with the other incremental values. The scarcity of softwood justified a premium of $\tfrac{9}{7}$, bringing the price up to $2 + \tfrac{9}{7} = 3\tfrac{2}{7}$ shillings per foot. Hardwood had no scarcity value, but the break-even cost of man-hours was $10 + \tfrac{1\frac{3}{7}}{} = 11\tfrac{6}{7}$ shillings per hour. Then every bookcase contains

$$12 \text{ feet of softwood at } 3\tfrac{2}{7} \text{ shillings} = 39\tfrac{3}{7} \text{ shillings}$$
$$1 \text{ foot of hardwood at } 5 \text{ shillings} = 5 \text{ shillings}$$
$$10 \text{ man-hours at } 11\tfrac{6}{7} \text{ shillings} = 118\tfrac{4}{7} \text{ shillings}$$
$$\text{Total price} = 163 \text{ shillings}$$
$$\text{Actual price} = 139 \text{ shillings}$$
$$\text{Difference} = \overline{24} \text{ shillings}$$

The difference is the increase in price needed to make book-cases compete on equal terms with the other two products for the productive resources available. At any higher price increase, such as the 25 shillings extra we chose, bookcases will have the advantage.

Exercise 4.13

An investigation into the unprofitability of bookcases has led to a new design, which would use 14 feet of softwood, 2 feet of hardwood and use 7 man-hours. What should its price be?

RANGES OF VALIDITY

We have already seen that the coefficient of r in equation (4.38) indicates an incremental value of $1\tfrac{3}{7}$, but this is only valid over a limited range of values of r. These values may be both positive and negative, for we shall lose profit by increasing r just as we gain it by letting r become negative. The other equations define the range of validity: in (4.34), if r takes on a negative value of -350, t will become zero and an equation will have to be transposed. The corresponding values from (4.35) and (4.36) are $-145\tfrac{5}{13}$ and $+14$, while (4.37) has no restrictive effect. The latter two values give the range of validity, and may be interpreted as follows.

If we make more man-hours available, then 'profit per foot of softwood' becomes more important than 'profit per man-hour', and consequently we find tables being replaced by chairs in the production plan. This would go on until all the tables had been replaced by chairs, thus consuming 350 extra man-hours, were it not for the fact that with $145\tfrac{5}{13}$ extra man-hours, we run out of hardwood. If, instead of making more man-hours available, we reduce the original figure of 270, chairs will be driven out of the solution in favour of tables, until all the chairs have gone.

Exercise 4.14

'It will pay us to expand the market for bookcases at a cost of not more than one shilling for each extra bookcase sold.'

At what point will this statement cease to be valid, in the solution equations (4.34) to (4.38)?

WORK FOR WORK'S SAKE?

It was pointed out in an earlier section that using 'minimum idle time' as a criterion may lead to fallacious results; so may such superficially laudable policies as 'keep all the customers satisfied'. The following example by Coaker[29] illustrates this.

John Smith runs a one-man woodworking business; he works an eight-hour day producing alpenstocks, bookshelves and chairs which sell at £3, £2 and £2 each respectively. He has the choice of working any one of three processes:

Process *P* costs £5 an hour to run, in which time it produces one alpenstock and two bookshelves.

Process *Q* costs £6 an hour, producing two alpenstocks and three chairs.

Process *R* costs £7 an hour, producing one alpenstock, one bookshelf and two chairs.

The local retailers have told Smith that they can sell anything up to nine alpenstocks, eleven bookshelves and nine chairs a day. How should he plan his work and how much profit will he make?

If we assume that our market must be fully satisfied and if *p*, *q* and *r* are the number of hours worked on the three processes, then

Number of alpenstocks made will be:

$$p + 2q + r = 9 \tag{4.39}$$

Number of bookshelves made will be:

$$2p + r = 11 \qquad (4.40)$$

Number of chairs made will be:

$$3q + 2r = 9 \qquad (4.41)$$

and solving these simultaneous equations will give us the answer $p = 4$ hours, $q = 1$ hour and $r = 3$ hours. The cost and revenue calculations show that Smith's profit will be £20 a day:

	£
Process P, 4 hours at £5	20
Process Q, 1 hour at £6	6
Process R, 3 hours at £7	21
	£47

Sale of alpenstocks, 9 at £3	27
Sale of bookshelves, 11 at £2	22
Sale of chairs, 9 at £2	18
	£67

giving £20 profit for 8 hours work.

If, however, we replace these equations by inequalities and select the solution which maximizes profit (easily calculated as £2 an hour on processes P and R and £6 an hour on Q), the problem becomes:

$$p + \ q + \ r \leqq 8 \qquad (4.42)$$
$$p + 2q + \ r \leqq 9 \qquad (4.43)$$
$$2p \ \ \ \ \ + \ r \leqq 11 \qquad (4.44)$$
$$3q + 2r \leqq 9 \qquad (4.45)$$

Maximize:

$$P = 2p + 6q + 2r \qquad (4.46)$$

for which the solution is:

$$s = 2 - \tfrac{2}{3}r + \ t - \tfrac{1}{3}v \qquad (4.47)$$
$$p = 3 + \tfrac{1}{3}r - \ t + \tfrac{2}{3}v \qquad (4.48)$$
$$u = 5 - \tfrac{5}{3}r + 2t - \tfrac{4}{3}v \qquad (4.49)$$
$$q = 3 - \tfrac{2}{3}r - \ \ \ \ \ \tfrac{1}{3}v \qquad (4.50)$$
$$P = 24 - \tfrac{4}{3}r - 2t - \tfrac{2}{3}v \qquad (4.51)$$

In this solution, s, t, u and v are the variables added to the left-hand sides of (4.42) to (4.45) respectively so that they become equations instead of inequalities.

		£
Process P, 3 hours at £5		15
Process Q, 3 hours at £6		18
Total cost		£33

Sale of alpenstocks, 9 at £3		27
Sale of bookshelves, 6 at £2		12
Sale of chairs, 9 at £2		18
Total revenue		£57

By working two hours less, Smith has increased his profit by £4.

Although this is a theoretical example, there is abundant evidence that some of the products with which manufacturers occupy their plant are unprofitable. The real-life problem is complicated by such considerations as setting-up times, the spreading of overheads, and the future pay-off from a currently unprofitable development; these may render the linear programming formulation more difficult, but do not necessarily invalidate it.

TACTICAL AND STRATEGIC APPLICATION

The first purpose to which we applied linear programming was finding the most efficient allocation of an existing set of limited resources. This we may call the tactical problem, and such problems are the essence of day-to-day management. However, the study of incremental costs led us to consider changing the availability of resources, as in making more man-hours available by authorizing overtime: these are strategic measures, generally associated with a higher level of management and the policy-making function. The contribution which linear programming makes in this second field may well prove to exceed in importance its already established usefulness in the tactical area.[30]

In the next chapter we shall go on to re-examine both these aspects of linear programming, but from a geometrical rather than an algebraic point of view.

4
Solutions to Exercises

Exercise 4.1

	Resources consumed		
	Softwood, ft	Hardwood, ft	Man-hours
10 bookcases	120	10	100
80 chairs	80	240	160
	200	250	260
Resources available	900	410	270

In each case, the resources consumed are less than the resources available, and therefore the plan is a feasible one.

Exercise 4.2

(a) Desks (15 shillings per unit)
(b) 54.
(c) £40 10s. 0d. (810 shillings).
(d) All the available man-hours have been used up.

Exercise 4.3

(a) Tables (4 shillings per man-hour).
(b) 90.
(c) £54 0s. 0d. (1,080 shillings).
(d) All the available man-hours have been used up.

Exercise 4.4
$$3t + 2c + 5d + 10b + r = 270.$$

r is a non-negative variable representing the number of man-hours available but not used.

Exercise 4.5
$$b \leq 10$$
i.e.
$$b + s = 10$$

in which s is the market capacity not taken up.

Exercise 4.6

$$P = 12t + 5c + 15d + 10b$$

Exercise 4.7

$$P = 5c + 15d + 10b + 1080 - 8c - 20d - 40b - 4r$$
$$= 1080 - 3c - 5d - 30b - 4r.$$

Exercise 4.8

$$P = 610 + 3t - c - 3r + 20s \quad \text{(from Figure 4.1)}$$

Exercise 4.9

$t = 70$	Make 70 tables.
$c = 30$	Make 30 chairs.
$\left.\begin{array}{l} d = 0 \\ b = 0 \end{array}\right\}$	Make no desks nor bookcases.
$p = 0$	No softwood is left over.
$q = 180$	Gives amount of hardwood left over.
$r = 0$	No man-hours are left over.
$s = 10$	The market capacity for bookcases is not taken up.
$P = 990$	Gives the profit in shillings.

Exercise 4.10

The extra variable representing the amount of softwood not used is p; its coefficient in (4.32) is $-\frac{9}{7}$; allowing p to take on a value of -1 would increase P by $\frac{9}{7}$ shillings, i.e. 1s. $3\frac{1}{2}$d., and we should be prepared to pay anything up to this figure.

Exercise 4.11

Nothing. Hardwood is not an operative restriction.

Exercise 4.12

	Softwood, ft	Man-hours
From 7 desks:	63	35
From 2 chairs:	2	4
Total	65	39
For 13 tables:	65	39

Exercise 4.13

£6 19s. 0d. i.e. 139 shillings as at present, given by:

	Incremental Value	Actual Cost
14 feet of softwood	46	28
2 feet of hardwood	10	10
7 man-hours	83	70
Total	139	108
Profit		31

Exercise 4.14

Expanding the market for bookcases means allowing s to take on negative values. The equations which restrict negative values of s are (4.34) and (4.36), the former giving $t = 0$ when $s = -25$, and the latter giving $c = 0$ when $s = -5$. The value put on market expansion is therefore valid only for an extra 5 bookcases.

NOTES AND REFERENCES

29 Battersby, A., *The Accountant*, 1 July 1961, p. 5, and 19 August 1961, p. 226.
30 Jewell, W., *Operations Research* (1960), vol. 8, No. 4, p. 565.
  The following books are recommended to the reader who wishes to pursue the subject of linear programming in greater detail:
31 Vajda, S., *Theory of Games and Linear Programming* (2nd edn, Methuen, 1962).
32 Vajda, S., *Readings in Mathematical Programming* (2nd edn, Pitman, 1962)—contains a good bibliography.
33 Gass, S. M., *Linear Programming* (2nd edn, McGraw-Hill, 1964). The original statement of the problem discussed in this chapter was given by Gass as Exercise 2 of his Chapter 1. He does not, however, give any solution to it.

5
Blending and Boundaries

The Kingdom of Number is all boundaries
Which may be beautiful and must be true;

W. H. AUDEN, *Numbers and Faces*

GEOMETRICAL REPRESENTATION

The Fermat Furniture example has been dealt with throughout by algebraic methods, but, as Chapter 3 suggested, problems of this type may also be represented geometrically. This will be shown by a new example from a different field of application of linear programming: blending. One of the earliest successful applications of the technique was to the production of commercial fuels by blending the outputs of an oil refinery, and it has also been used to find the cheapest way of making food mixtures, and to investigate the cost of diets.

A PROBLEM IN BLENDING

The Weasel Oil Company is a small business which specializes in blending oil for Weasel engines, to the following specification:

Specific Gravity	at least 0·88
Viscosity	not more than 32 units
Sulphur	not more than 0·35%

The sulphur and viscosity figures in this and the other specifications have been corrected for specific gravity so that any blending calculations can be done directly by volume. We can also assume that all the specification figures blend according to linear rules. For example, one gallon of oil with viscosity 40 units blended into one gallon with viscosity 44 units will yield a blend with viscosity 42 units.

The company holds a stock of 100,000 gallons of oil with the following characteristics:—

Specific Gravity	0·89
Viscosity	20 units
Sulphur	0·30%

and the manager wants to increase his stock by blending without going outside the specification. To do so, he can blend in Boozle Oil or Fizzle Oil, which he can buy at the same price per gallon. Boozle Oil is available in unlimited quantities, but the manager can only buy up to 90,000 gallons of Fizzle Oil.

What is the greatest amount of Weasel Oil that he can make by blending, if the oils available for blending have the following specifications?

	Boozle Oil	Fizzle Oil
Specific Gravity	0·92	0·86
Viscosity	44	40
Sulphur	0·45	0·25

USING SUBSCRIPTS

To solve this problem algebraically, we must first express it as a set of linear equations and a function to be maximized or minimized. It can then be dealt with by manipulating the equations as shown in the previous chapter, so that the 'profit', or in this case the total amount of blended oil, is brought step by step to its maximum value.

This is an opportune point at which to learn a bit of mathematical notation which is not generally dealt with in schools, that is, the use of subscripts. We could call the amounts of Boozle Oil and Fizzle Oil b and f respectively, just as we denoted tables and chairs by their initials in the last chapter. However, since they both represent the same *sort* of variable – quantities of oil – professional mathematicians prefer to use the symbols x_1 and x_2, where 1 and 2 are called subscripts. The symbol x_1 is pronounced 'x-one' or sometimes 'x-sub-one'.

Exercise 5.1

Rewrite the inequality (4.1) in the previous chapter, using x_1 for tables, x_2 for chairs, x_3 for desks and x_4 for bookcases.

Exercise 5.2

Rewrite equation (4.2), allocating the subscript 5 to the variable previously represented by p.

Exercise 5.3

In the equations (4.3), (4.4) and (4.5), what new symbols would you suggest substituting for q, r and s respectively?

The mathematician uses subscripts for convenience and not, as you may have suspected, to make his work more difficult to understand. Remember that he will be dealing with much bigger equations than the ones used here, and ask yourself what you would do if the Fermat Furniture Co. made a hundred different items instead of four. With subscripts, one has only to call them x_1, x_2, x_3 and so on up to x_{100} (and there are other benefits such as the ability to reduce long equations to simple shorthand forms with the aid of signs like Σ, 'the sum of').

If x_1 and x_2 represent the amounts of Boozle Oil and Fizzle Oil respectively, in units of 1,000 gallons, then since we have to maximize the total amount P of blend produced:

$$P = 100 + x_1 + x_2 \qquad (5.1)$$

The specific gravity of the mixed oils will be:

$$\frac{0 \cdot 89 \times 100 + 0 \cdot 92x_1 + 0 \cdot 86x_2}{100 + x_1 + x_2} \geqq 0 \cdot 88$$

Multiplying both sides by the denominator gives:

$$89 + 0 \cdot 92x_1 + 0 \cdot 86x_2 \geqq 88 + 0 \cdot 88x_1 + 0 \cdot 88x_2$$

which reduces to

$$1 + 0 \cdot 04x_1 - 0 \cdot 02x_2 \geqq 0$$

Multiplying throughout by 50 gives:

$$50 + 2x_1 - x_2 \geqq 0$$

which is transposed to

$$-2x_1 + x_2 \leqq 50 \qquad (5.2)$$

Note that in manipulating these inequalities we used some of the rules applicable to equations, such as that the expression is still valid if equal quantities are added or subtracted on both sides of the inequality sign, or if all the terms in the expression are multiplied or divided by the same positive factor.

Exercise 5.4

Draw a graph of the inequality (5.2) for non-negative values of x_1 and x_2. (See Figure 3.4.) Label the appropriate areas 'S.G. outside specification' and 'S.G. within specification'.

The corresponding equations for viscosity and sulphur are respectively

$$\frac{20 \times 100 + 44x_1 + 40x_2}{100 + x_1 + x_2} \leqq 32$$

and

$$\frac{0 \cdot 30 \times 100 + 0 \cdot 45x_1 + 0 \cdot 25x_2}{100 + x_1 + x_2} \leqq 0 \cdot 35$$

which reduce to

$$3x_1 + 2x_2 \leqq 300 \qquad (5.3)$$

and

$$x_1 - x_2 \leqq 50 \qquad (5.4)$$

We can now assemble these expressions, including the restriction on Fizzle Oil, into the complete algebraic statement of the problem. (The variable x_3 is reserved for use later.)

$$-2x_1 + x_2 + x_4 = 50 \qquad (5.5)$$
$$3x_1 + 2x_2 + x_5 = 300 \qquad (5.6)$$
$$x_1 - x_2 + x_6 = 50 \qquad (5.7)$$
$$x_2 + x_7 = 90 \qquad (5.8)$$

Maximize $\qquad P = 100 + x_1 + x_2 \qquad (5.1)$

The four restrictions (5.5) to (5.8) can be drawn as graphs, and this has been done in Figure 5.1. In the top right-hand corner is shown the quadrant within which all the values of x_1 and x_2 must lie, and the shading indicates the areas within which they must not lie if they are to be non-negative. The next graph down, (b), shows the restriction imposed by equation (5.8): the shaded area above the horizontal line corresponds to blends containing more than 90,000 gallons of Fizzle Oil, which are not feasible. In the third graph, (c), the oblique line corresponds to equation (5.6) when x_5 is held equal to zero; it is therefore the graph of $3x_1 + 2x_2 = 300$.

Exercise 5.5

Using the equation $3x_1 + 2x_2 = 300$, find

    (i) x_1 when $x_2 = 0$
    (ii) x_2 when $x_1 = 0$
    (iii) x_1 and x_2 when they are equal.

Check that they all lie on the straight line in Figure 5.1(c)

Exercise 5.6

In equation (5.6), what is the value of x_5 when

    (i) $x_1 = 50$, $x_2 = 75$
    (ii) $x_1 = 50$, $x_2 = 50$
    (iii) $x_1 = 100$, $x_2 = 100$?

Check that negative values of x_5 correspond to points outside the feasible area, and positive values to points within it.

It is worth spending a little time on Figure 5.1, so as to make yourself familiar with the idea of feasible and non-feasible areas, which are finally combined to give the total solution area. It is the irregular hexagonal space in the middle and it contains all the feasible blends, from which the best is to be chosen – that is, the blend which maximizes P in the control equation (5.1). The equation for this control function represents a family of parallel straight lines, each member of which has a gradient of -1. The value of P increases as the line moves away from the origin. Figure 5.2 shows a set of these lines drawn for various values of P, and we can see that the best blend is that for which $P = 230$, when $x_1 = 40$ and $x_2 = 90$.

Fig. 5.1 A problem in blending: graphical solution
(1) restrictions

The corresponding algebraic solution is:

$$x_4 = 40 \quad - \tfrac{2}{3}x_5 + \tfrac{7}{3}x_7 \qquad (5.9)$$

$$x_2 = 90 \qquad\qquad - x_7 \qquad (5.10)$$

$$x_1 = 40 \quad - \tfrac{1}{3}x_5 + \tfrac{2}{3}x_7 \qquad (5.11)$$

$$x_6 = 100 + \tfrac{1}{3}x_5 - \tfrac{5}{3}x_7 \qquad (5.12)$$

$$P = 230 - \tfrac{1}{3}x_5 - \tfrac{1}{3}x_7 \qquad (5.13)$$

The additional variables are x_4 to x_7. Every item in the
algebraic solution has its counterpart in the graphical one.
The two operative restrictions are seen to be on viscosity and
on the quantity of Fizzle Oil; Figure 5.3 shows the incremental
value of the latter to be

$$\frac{233\tfrac{1}{3} - 230}{100 - 90} = \tfrac{1}{3}$$

(a) quantity

restrictions on x_1 and x_2:
they must be non-negative
so they must lie in this
quadrant only

(b) quantity

restriction on x_2:
it must not exceed 90

(c) quality

restriction
on viscosity:
$3x_1 + 2x_2$
must not exceed 300

(d) quality

restriction on S G:
$2x_1 - x_2 \leqq 50$

restriction on sulphur:
$x_1 - x_2 = 50$

which may also be obtained from the coefficient of x_7 in
equation (5.13). Point Z, at which specific gravity becomes an
operative restriction, is one limit of the range of validity for
this incremental value.

Suppose that, instead of an upper limit on Fizzle Oil, we
impose a lower limit of not less than 150,000 gallons to be

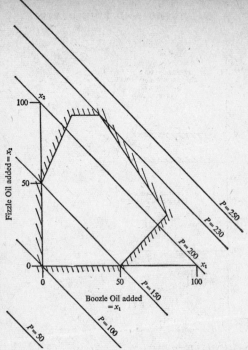

Fig. 5.2 A problem in blending: graphical solution
(2) function to be maximized; (3) possible routes to final solution

added. Then it is immediately apparent from Figure 5.4 that there is no feasible solution to the problem, because all the blends above the lower limit infringe the quality specifications.

Exercise 5.7

Use Figure 5.2 to find the optimum solution to the blending problem with the restrictions on viscosity and quantity of Fizzle Oil removed.

Exercise 5.8

If the profit on every 1,000 gallons of Boozle Oil added is £3, and is £2 on every 1,000 gallons of either Fizzle Oil or the existing stock,

(a) write down the new profit function
(b) find an optimum solution graphically.

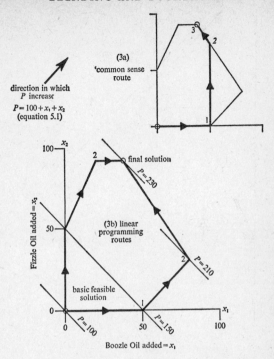

ROUTE TO THE SOLUTION

Figure 5.5 shows the part of Figure 5.2 in the region near the origin, but the drawing has been rotated through $45°$ so that the control function P appears as a horizontal line. Increasing x_1 from zero is equivalent to moving along the line OA, and the vertex A is the point at which equation (5.4) restricts any further improvement in P. Similarly, increasing x_2 takes us along OB to B, the specific gravity restriction. The rates of increase of P with x_1 and x_2 are the same, which may be seen algebraically because x_1 and x_2 have the same coefficient in the control function, and geometrically because they have the same gradient in Figure 5.5. The usual practice in solving linear programming problems is to begin by increasing the

Fig. 5.3 Effect of changing restriction on x_2

term with the greatest coefficient, i.e. the steepest gradient. The gradients being the same in this case, we shall arbitrarily select x_2 and move to the vertex B. The route to the solution consists of a number of such moves along edges to vertices, choosing only such edges as have an upward gradient (or sometimes a horizontal one) – that is, choosing only terms with positive coefficients in the control function. The solution is found at the summit, from which all routes lead downwards (or, in rare cases, horizontally as in Exercise 5.8).

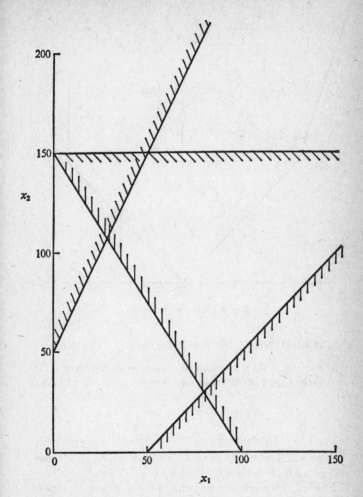

Fig. 5.4 Blending problem with lower limit on Fizzle Oil and no feasible solutions

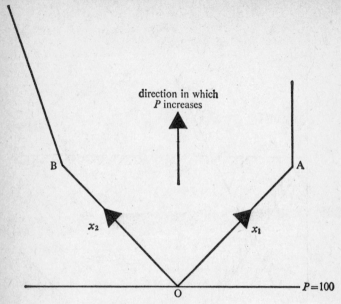

Fig. 5.5 Choice of routes

BLENDING THREE OR MORE ADDITIVES

Suppose that a third component, Muzzle Oil, becomes available to the extent of 60,000 gallons if required. Its specification is:

Specific Gravity	0·87
Viscosity	36 units
Sulphur	0·40%

A graphical solution will now extend into three dimensions, one for each of the quantities x_1, x_2 and x_3.

Instead of the restrictions being lines bounding an area of feasibility, they are now planes enclosing a solution space, which will be a convex polyhedron. Two views of the polyhedron are given in Figure 5.7 and 5.8. All blends which satisfy the specification are contained within this irregular octahedron, and in each figure it is cut by a plane corresponding

Fig. 5.7 Three-dimensional model

to the profit P, which is shown at an intermediate value. As this plane moves outwards from the origin, it eventually reaches a single vertex to which the final solution corresponds. In this instance the solution is:

Boozle Oil: $x_1 = 28\frac{4}{7}$ i.e. 28,571 gallons
Fizzle Oil: $x_2 = 77\frac{1}{7}$ i.e. 77,143 gallons
Muzzle Oil: $x_3 = 60$ i.e. 60,000 gallons
Total Blend $P = 265$ i.e. 265,714 gallons

The solution is again reached by starting from the origin and moving along the edges to successive vertices, always in a direction which improves P, to the final solution. (Figure 4.1 was a symbolic representation of different routes around a polyhedron, with the boxes representing conditions at its

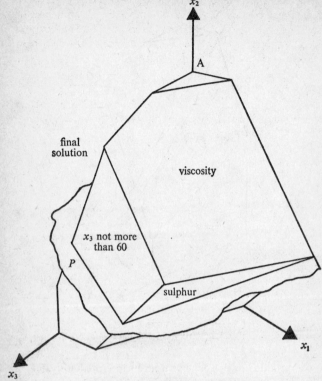

Fig. 5.8 Three-dimensional model

vertices.) Although the problem with two additives could have been solved easily by trial and error, it is unlikely that any approach other than linear programming would solve the three-dimensional problem.

When the number of variables exceeds three, a complete graph of the solution cannot be drawn, although for four variables we could represent the process of solution by a series of three-dimensional solid bodies showing successive cross-sections of the solution space when cut by the 'hyper-plane' of *P*.

The reader who finds such excursions into many dimensions interesting would be well advised to read Abbott's light-hearted essay 'Flatland', originally published in 1890 but recently re-issued.[34] It is strange to reflect on the relevance of this fantasy to the daily operation of an oil refinery.

Exercise 5.9

Draw a rough sketch of the control function in the problem of the Fermat Furniture Company ignoring bookcases, i.e.

$$P = 12t + 5c + 15d$$

for the value $P = 60$.

TABLEAUX

If we were to ask an Organization and Methods expert to study the linear programming calculations, he might well point out that there is a good deal of time wasted in carrying out the calculations as previously described. He would probably say 'Do you have to write all those x's down every time? Why not just make a column of the coefficients and write the appropriate x at the top of it?' By following this advice we arrive at a presentation known as a 'Tableau'. A simple tableau corresponding to equations (5.1) and (5.5) to (5.8) is given below:

Quantity	x_1	x_2		
50	-2	$+1$	x_4	(5.5)
300	$+3$	$+2$	x_5	(5.6)
50	$+1^*$	-1	x_6	(5.7)
90	0	$+1$	x_7	(5.8)
100	-1	-1	P	(5.1)

The equations have again been transposed, but if we read the double vertical line as an 'equals' sign, we can see that they correspond to those whose numbers appear in brackets alongside.

We arrive at the final solution, as before, in a series of steps. At each step, the tableau is transformed into a new one by a set of systematic rules. These rules correspond exactly to the rearrangement of the equations as already described in Chapter 4. The first rule is to look in the bottom row to the right of the double line and pick out the greatest number which is preceded by a negative sign. In this case, we can choose either x_1 or x_2, and have arbitrarily begun with x_1. We next look for positive coefficients in the column above, and for each of these we divide the figure in the 'Quantity' column by the coefficient: the ratios obtained in this way are 100 and 50, as before. The coefficient corresponding to the smaller result is selected, and is called the 'pivot': it is marked with an asterisk in the tableau above. Once the pivot has been identified, the variable above it (in this case x_1) is interchanged with the variable alongside it (x_6). We can then transform the tableau, and need only four rules to do this (assuming that certain fairly rare complications do not occur):

For the row which contains the pivot

(1) Replace the pivot itself by its own reciprocal.

(2) For all the other coefficients in this row, divide the original value by the pivot to obtain the new value.

For all the other rows (including the 'P' row)

(3) For any coefficient in the same column as the pivot, divide the original value by the pivot and reverse the sign.

(4) For each of the other coefficients, draw an imaginary rectangle with the coefficient at one corner and the pivot diagonally opposite (as they appear in the old tableau).

Fig. 5.12

(a) Multiply 'above the pivot' by 'alongside the pivot'.

(b) Divide the product so obtained by the pivot.

(c) Subtract the quotient from the coefficient to obtain the new value of the coefficient.

These rules apply to the coefficients in the Quantity column and those in the 'P' row as well as the others. The second tableau, derived by these rules, is given below.

Quantity	x_6	x_2	
150	$+2$	-1	x_4
150	-3	$+5$	x_5
50	$+1$	-1	x_1
90	0	$+1$	x_7
150	$+1$	-2	P

Exercise 5.10

Write out in full the set of equations corresponding to the tableau immediately above.

The tableaux have been presented like this in order to show as closely as possible their relationship to the sets of simultaneous equations discussed earlier. In this form, they are rather a hodge-podge because some of the variables appear along the top and some down the right-hand side. A more usual form of presentation is the Simplex tableau in which all the variables have columns allocated to them. The rules for manipulating these tableaux differ slightly from those already given, because each column now corresponds to one and only one variable throughout the whole set of calculations. The rules are:

(i) Select the pivot as before.

(ii) Divide the numbers in the row containing the pivot by the value of the pivot itself.

(iii) Replace all the remaining numbers in the column containing the pivot by zero.

(iv) For each of the other coefficients, use the 'rectangle' rule (4) above.

The Simplex tableaux corresponding to those given above are in Table 5.1, which also gives the two subsequent iterations leading to the final solutions.

TABLE 5.1

Simplex Tableaux of the Two-Dimensional Problem

First Tableau

Quantity	x_1	x_2	x_4	x_5	x_6	x_7
50	−2	+1	+1	0	0	0
300	+3	+2	0	+1	0	0
50	+1*	−1	0	0	+1	0
90	0	+1	0	0	0	+1
100	−1	−1	0	0	0	0

Second Tableau

Quantity	x_1	x_2	x_4	x_5	x_6	x_7
150	0	−1	+1	0	+2	0
150	0	+5*	0	+1	−3	0
50	+1	−1	0	0	+1	0
90	0	+1	0	0	0	+1
150	0	−2	0	0	+1	0

Third Tableau

Quantity	x_1	x_2	x_4	x_5	x_6	x_7
180	0	0	+1	$+\frac{1}{5}$	$+\frac{7}{5}$	0
30	0	+1	0	$+\frac{1}{5}$	$-\frac{3}{5}$	0
80	+1	0	0	$+\frac{1}{5}$	$+\frac{2}{5}$	0
60	0	0	0	$-\frac{1}{5}$	$+\frac{3}{5}$*	+1
210	0	0	0	$+\frac{2}{5}$	$-\frac{1}{5}$	0

Fourth Tableau (optimum solution)

Quantity	x_1	x_2	x_4	x_5	x_6	x_7
40	0	0	+1	$+\frac{2}{3}$	0	$-\frac{7}{3}$
90	0	+1	0	0	0	+1
40	+1	0	0	$+\frac{1}{3}$	0	$-\frac{2}{3}$
100	0	0	0	$-\frac{1}{3}$	+1	$+\frac{5}{3}$
230	0	0	0	$+\frac{1}{3}$	0	$+\frac{1}{3}$

Exercise 5.11

Set up a Simplex tableau for the Fermat Furniture problem, using equations (4.6) to (4.10) inclusive as a starting point.

Exercise 5.12

Set up and solve the Simplex tableau for the blending problem with three additives. (Start from Table 5.1, inserting extra colums for x_3 and x_8. Use variable x_1 as the first pivot.)

SOME PRACTICAL APPLICATIONS OF LINEAR PROGRAMMING

Wyatt[35] has given an interesting factual account of a blending problem in the Glacier Metal Company Ltd which makes white metal bearings. The problem was to blend the maximum value of recovered melt with virgin tin, antimony, copper and lead in making up alloys to required specifications, that is, to maximize a function F such that

$$F = m_1 x_1 + m_2 x_2 + m_3 x_3 + m_4 x_4$$

(Note that in this equation the use of subscripts has been extended to the coefficients m by which the variables x are to be multiplied.)

The m's are the values per pound of the recovered melts and the x's are the weights used. There were two types of restriction: those on weight of the general form $x_1 \leqq W_1$, W_1 being the weight of melt available, and those of the form

$$t_1 x_1 + t_2 x_2 + t_3 x_3 + t_4 x_4 \leqq T,$$

with T as the total weight of tin required, and the t's representing the tin contents of the recovered melts.

The tableau contained about a dozen variables, and, as already mentioned, was solved by a girl with an electric desk-calculating machine. About 5 per cent more recovered metal was utilized with the aid of linear programming, giving a worthwhile saving. Moreover, a 'bonus' was obtained in the form of a quicker turnover of the recovered metal, with consequently lower stocks.

Dr Morton of the London School of Economics has described[36] how linear programming was introduced into an Indian textile mill as a means of planning production for maximum profit. Much of his work was devoted to reducing a potentially huge tableau to manageable size: for instance, he found it possible to reduce the total production flow to a small range of possible 'bottlenecks'; 40 principal products were selected from the full list of 400; 100 different kinds of loom were sorted into 12 groups. The final set of equations contained about 160 columns and 20 rows, the latter corresponding to the restrictions; they were solved without the aid of an electronic computer.

Morton deals with some of the J-factors introduced:

If some kind of equipment is not restrictive under a given solution, if, e.g. an extra spindle hour could not increase total profits because spindles were not fully used, the apparent contribution of the spinning department to profits appears to be nil. It raises the question how to counteract the psychological effect of partly understood numerical details, or perhaps how to keep certain items of information from middle grade management. This is also related to the difficulty of persuading management that it may be better to keep certain items of equipment idle.

and again

The only risk is the well-known, psychological one of assuming accurate knowledge merely because a number has been put on paper.

Koenigsberg[37] has compared the costs of different computers in solving a problem in the plywood industry. The function to be maximized was the total return from the products manufactured under restrictions on raw material, market and plant capacity: the resulting tableau contained about 50 equations and 100 variables, and the computer times and costs are given in Table 5.2.

He quotes two other problems in the same paper, one concerning the distribution of grain and the other a fermentation process in which a production schedule is drawn up over several successive periods. Amongst his pertinent comments are the following:

... in all three instances, the linear programming study was carried out for companies that were relatively small. The solutions yielded very worthwhile results in real terms, showing that the technique does not necessarily have to be applied to very large-scale operations to be effective.

Experience has shown that merely the process of writing down the pertinent relations in an operation leads to a better understanding of the industry itself as well as of the problem.

TABLE 5.2

Machine	Time	Cost/hour	Total cost	Remarks
IBM 650	16 hr	$50	$800–1,280	No tape
Burroughs 205	2¾ hr	$100–150	$275–415	Tape
Burroughs 220	5 min.	$300–400	$30–40	Min. charge is for 1/10 hr
Philco 2000	1 min.	$375	$37·50	Min. charge is for 1/10 hr
IBM 704	6 min.	$300–500	$30–50	Min. charge is for 1/10 hr
Ferranti Mercury	5 min.	£75	£7	

Further, the process of solution always provides more information than just giving the solution itself. The formulations may therefore change with the passage of time as the operational research worker and the manager learn to understand one another and both learn more about the complex relationships between the variables of the industrial pattern.

Published work dealing with oil refineries is fairly extensive, and papers by Catchpole[38] and Newby and Deam[39] are noteworthy. The latter deals in detail with the conditions under which a production schedule is compiled for a single oil refinery, and the former shows how integrated operations render the problem even more complex and introduces some difficulties brought about by the sheer size of the matrix.

The installation of a planning system in a food factory is the subject of a paper by Jones and Rope of Fisons' Limited.[40] The factory manufactures ten different food products by nine different processes from two basic raw materials which are highly perishable and have a highly seasonal pattern of availability. Two models are used for planning, one covering six successive periods of one month each, the other adding two further periods of three months each.

The restrictions considered include those on production, maximum and minimum stock levels, availability of raw material and certain contractual obligations. The control function was essentially an expression for maximizing profit, but it needed to be modified in various ways. Products for which a sales forecast has been made will have a constant expected revenue from sales, and, since the cost of raw material is the principal variable element in their manufacture, a function which minimizes this cost is adequate. Other products are essentially users of residual raw materials, and their contributions have to be taken as expected gross profit margins. Stock-holding costs are included, including the hiring of outside warehousing space if necessary.

Much careful thought has to be put into a practical formulation. One can easily over-complicate a model, and the manager and mathematician must collaborate closely to decide not only what is relevant, but what is significant.[41-5] For instance, Jones and Rope say that they first tried to incorporate restrictions specifically based on types of labour available, but abandoned them: limitation of the allowable range of production rates on groups of related plants was found to be a far more effective way of controlling labour requirements. Their model is being extended to embrace several factories linked by a network of transportation facilities. The latter may be dealt with by a particular form of the linear programming model which is the subject of the next chapter.

5
Solutions to Exercises

Exercise 5.1
$$5x_1 + x_2 + 9x_3 + 12x_4 \leqq 900$$

Exercise 5.2
$$5x_1 + x_2 + 9x_3 + 12x_4 + x_5 = 900$$

Exercise 5.3
$$q = x_6 \qquad r = x_7 \qquad s = x_8$$

Exercise 5.4

Exercise 5.5

  (i) $x_1 = 100, \quad x_2 = 0$
  (ii) $x_1 = 0, \qquad x_2 = 150$
  (iii) $x_1 = 60, \qquad x_2 = 60$

Exercise 5.6

  (i) $x_5 = 0$

  (ii) $x_5 = +50$

  (iii) $x_5 = -200$

Exercise 5.7

P can be made as large as we choose; there are no operative restrictions and therefore there is no single solution. In geometric terms, we can put the P-line at an infinite distance from the origin.

Exercise 5.8

  (a) $P = 200 + 3x_1 + 2x_2$

  (b) The profit function has the same gradient as the

sulphur restriction, and coincides with it when P is maximized. Any pair of values between A and B generates an optimum case; for example $x_1 = 60$, $x_2 = 60$ gives $P = 500$.

Exercise 5.9

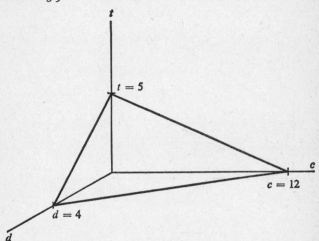

Exercise 5.10

$$x_4 = 150 + x_2 - 2x_6$$
$$x_5 = 150 - 5x_2 + 3x_6$$
$$x_1 = 50 + x_2 - x_6$$
$$x_7 = 90 - x_2$$
$$P = 150 + 2x_2 - x_6$$

Note that in this case the area of feasible solutions is defined by only three restrictions. Those who wish to delve more deeply into the relationship between geometric and algebraic methods may like to study the figure below and ponder its implications. It is the graph of this set of equations.

Exercise 5.11

Let $x_1 = t,$ $x_2 = c,$ $x_3 = d,$ $x_4 = b$
       $x_5 = p,$ $x_6 = q,$ $x_7 = r,$ $x_8 = s$

Q	x_1	x_2	x_3	x_4	x_5	x_6	x_7	x_8
900	$+5$	$+1$	$+9$	$+12$	$+1$	0	0	0
410	$+2$	$+3$	$+4$	$+1$	0	$+1$	0	0
270	$+3$	$+2$	$+5$	$+10$	0	0	$+1$	0
10	0	0	0	$+1$	0	0	0	$+1$
0	-12	-5	-15	-10	0	0	0	0

Exercise 5.12
First Tableau

	Q	x_1	x_2	x_3	x_4	x_5	x_6	x_7	x_8
x_4	100	-4	$+2$	$+1$	$+1$	0	0	0	0
x_5	300	$+3$	$+2$	$+1$	0	$+1$	0	0	0
x_6	100	$+2^*$	-2	$+1$	0	0	$+1$	0	0
x_7	90	0	$+1$	0	0	0	0	$+1$	0
x_8	60	0	0	$+1$	0	0	0	0	$+1$
	100	-1	-1	-1	0	0	0	0	0

Second Tableau

	Q	x_1	x_2	x_3	x_4	x_5	x_6	x_7	x_8
x_4	300	0	-2	$+3$	$+1$	0	$+2$	0	0
x_5	150	0	$+5^*$	$-\frac{1}{2}$	0	$+1$	$-\frac{3}{2}$	0	0
x_1	50	$+1$	-1	$+\frac{1}{2}$	0	0	$+\frac{1}{2}$	0	0
x_7	90	0	$+1$	0	0	0	0	$+1$	0
x_8	60	0	0	$+1$	0	0	0	0	$+1$
	150	0	-2	$-\frac{1}{2}$	0	0	$+\frac{1}{2}$	0	0

Third Tableau

	Q	x_1	x_2	x_3	x_4	x_5	x_6	x_7	x_8
x_4	360	0	0	$+\frac{14}{5}$	$+1$	$+\frac{2}{5}$	$+\frac{7}{5}$	0	0
x_2	30	0	$+1$	$-\frac{1}{10}$	0	$+\frac{1}{5}$	$-\frac{3}{10}$	0	0
x_1	80	$+1$	0	$+\frac{2}{5}$	0	$+\frac{1}{5}$	$+\frac{1}{5}$	0	0
x_7	60	0	0	$+\frac{1}{10}$	0	$-\frac{1}{5}$	$+\frac{3}{10}$	$+1$	0
x_8	60	0	0	$+1^*$	0	0	0	0	$+1$
	210	0	0	$-\frac{7}{10}$	0	$+\frac{2}{5}$	$-\frac{1}{10}$	0	0

Fourth Tableau

	Q	x_1	x_2	x_3	x_4	x_5	x_6	x_7	x_8
x_4	192	0	0	0	$+1$	$+\frac{2}{5}$	$+\frac{7}{5}^*$	0	$-\frac{14}{5}$
x_2	36	0	$+1$	0	0	$+\frac{1}{5}$	$-\frac{3}{10}$	0	$+\frac{1}{10}$
x_1	56	$+1$	0	0	0	$+\frac{1}{5}$	$+\frac{1}{5}$	0	$-\frac{2}{5}$
x_7	54	0	0	0	0	$-\frac{1}{5}$	$+\frac{3}{10}$	$+1$	$-\frac{1}{10}$
x_3	60	0	0	$+1$	0	0	0	0	$+1$
	252	0	0	0	0	$+\frac{2}{5}$	$-\frac{1}{10}$	0	$+\frac{7}{10}$

Fifth Tableau

	Q	x_1	x_2	x_3	x_4	x_5	x_6	x_7	x_8
x_6	$137\frac{1}{2}$	0	0	0	$+7$	$+\frac{2}{7}$	$+1$	0	-2
x_2	$77\frac{1}{2}$	0	$+1$	0	$+4$	$+\frac{2}{7}$	0	0	$-\frac{1}{2}$
x_1	$28\frac{4}{7}$	$+1$	0	0	$-\frac{1}{7}$	$+\frac{1}{7}$	0	0	0
x_7	$12\frac{6}{7}$	0	0	0	$-\frac{3}{14}$	$-\frac{2}{7}$	0	$+1$	$+\frac{1}{2}$
x_3	60	0	0	$+1$	0	0	0	0	$+1$
	$265\frac{5}{7}$	0	0	0	$+\frac{1}{14}$	$+\frac{1}{35}$	0	0	$+\frac{1}{2}$

This is the final solution.

NOTES AND REFERENCES

34 Abbott, E. A., *Flatland: a Romance of Many Dimensions* (Blackwell, 1950).

35 Wyatt, J. K., *Operational Research Quarterly* (1958), vol. 9, No. 2, p. 154.

36 Morton, G., *Operational Research Quarterly* (1958), vol. 9, No. 3, p. 198.

37 Koenigsberg, E., *Operational Research Quarterly* (1961), vol. 12, No. 2, p. 105.

38 Catchpole, A. R., *Operational Research Quarterly* (1962), vol. 13, No. 2, p. 163.

39 Newby, W. J., and Deam, R. J., *Planning for Productivity in the Oil Industry* (The Institute of Petroleum), p. 68.

40 Jones, W. G., and Rope, C. M., *Operational Research Quarterly* (1964), vol. 15, No. 4, p. 293.

Other useful references include:

41 Charnes, A., Cooper, W. W., and Mellon, B., *Econometrica* (1952), vol. 20, No. 2.

42 Brigham, G., *Operations Research* (1959), vol. 7, 524–33.

43 Jewell, W. S., *Operations Research* (1960), vol. 8, 565–70.

44 Dantzig, G. B., *Linear Programming and Extensions* (Princeton University Press, 1963), chap. 27.

45 Brown, J. A. C., *Symposium on Linear Programming* (1954), Ferranti Ltd., London.

Transportation by Tabulation

Lines, circles, scenes, letters and characters;
Ay, these are those that Faustus most desires.
Oh, what a world of profit and delight,
Of power, of honour, of omnipotence
Is promis'd to the studious artisan!

MARLOWE, *Dr Faustus*

CERTAIN complex problems in distributing goods may be reduced to a simple routine; it will be described arithmetically in this chapter, but we shall not bother with the theoretical justification, contenting ourselves with the comment that it is a special case of the linear programming method already described. The Heinz Company in the U.S.A. was a pioneer in the industrial application of this method, which was originally devised for planning convoys across the Atlantic in the Second World War. One large oil company is also using it to decide which distribution areas in Western Europe should be allocated to each of the refineries it controls.

The Pythagoras Processed Plankton Co. is an imaginary enterprise operating in the future when much of our protein intake may be harvested from the sea. This company owns factories at the four ports where its edible plankton is landed and processed; they are –

Amsterdam	Capacity	50,000	tons per year
Barcelona	,,	72,000	,,
Copenhagen	,,	57,000	,,
Dieppe	,,	21,000	,,
Total		200,000	

It also has five main centres for distribution to the European market, which are listed below together with their estimated annual demand:

Milan	36,000 tons per year
Paris	69,000	,,
Rome	35,000	,,
Strasbourg	20,000	,,
Turin	40,000	,,
Total	200,000

A map of the factories and market centres is given in Figure 6.1.

Fig. 6.1 Centres of manufacture and distribution for Pythagoras' Processed Plankton

The company runs its own fleet of delivery vehicles, which have a uniform cost of one shilling per mile. The Transport Manager has the problem of deciding how the factories and distribution centres are to be linked to each other so that the cost of distribution is as low as possible. His first job is to compile a table of distances, Table 6.1.

TABLE 6.1

Distances between Plankton Factories and Centres
(in miles, single journey only)

| Factory | Market Centre | | | | |
	Milan	Paris	Rome	Strasbourg	Turin
Amsterdam	678	307	1,059	363	683
Barcelona	648	685	887	684	564
Copenhagen	937	731	1,248	631	982
Dieppe	639	103	1,016	367	602

(The figures in this table were taken from the Automobile Association's Foreign Touring Guide, 1963.)

His present method is to begin with the centre of highest demand, Paris, and allocate as much as possible from the nearest factory, Dieppe. Its capacity is not enough, so he completes the Paris allocation from the next nearest factory, which is Amsterdam. When he has satisfied Paris, he selects the next biggest market, Turin, and proceeds in the same way. Eventually he arrives at the 'common-sense' allocation shown in Table 6.2.

TABLE 6.2

Plankton Allocation. First 'Common-Sense' Solution
(in thousands of tons)

| Factory | Market Centre | | | | | |
	Milan	Paris	Rome	Strasbourg	Turin	Total
Amsterdam	2	48				50
Barcelona	32				40	72
Copenhagen	2		35	20		57
Dieppe		21				21
Total	36	69	35	20	40	200

The total ton-mileage (not counting return journeys) is 119,725 which at two shillings per mile (out-and-return) would cost £11,972,500. Can this total be reduced?

This is an allocation problem, and may be solved by linear

programming. We can set up linear equations (or inequalities) to ensure that no factory is called on to distribute more than it can produce and that no market receives more than it can sell; we then have to minimize a total cost function, made up of individual terms like the following:

Amount supplied to Milan from Amsterdam ×
  Cost of supplying a unit amount to Milan from Amsterdam.

For the common-sense solution in Table 6.2, this term would be

$$(2000 \times 2) \times 678 \text{ shillings}$$

where the multiplier 2000 is needed because of the double journey and the use of thousands of tons as a unit in Table 6.2.

Exercise 6.1

In Table 6.2, what terms would express the costs of supplying

(i) Milan from Barcelona?
(ii) Rome from Amsterdam?

Exercise 6.2

If we minimize the ton-mileage, shall we automatically minimize the cost in this example?

Exercise 6.3

Use the values in Tables 6.1 and 6.2 to check that the total mileage of 119,725,000 in the 'common-sense' solution is correct.

The problem could be solved by the algebraic methods already described, but it has a special property which makes an even simpler routine possible: all the variables in the equations turn out to have unit coefficients, giving what is known as a 'transportation matrix'. (A matrix is a rectangular array of numbers.) One of these simple routines is called the method of 'fictitious costs'. It starts from any feasible solution – we shall use Table 6.2 as a starting-point – and improve it in successive iterations until a demonstrable optimum is found.

It must be emphasized here that the 'fictitious costs' are **a** technical term for an aid to calculation and have no real meaning in the accountants' sense.

For convenience, we shall from now on refer to individual entries as being in the 'cells' of the matrix; each cell will be described by the initials of the factory and the market corresponding to it. For instance, the entry in cell *CR* of Table 6.1 is 1,248.

First we can simplify the matrix of mileages (i.e. costs) in Table 6.1 so as to ease the subsequent burden of arithmetic. The first row gives all the distances from Amsterdam, the shortest being 307 miles to Paris. This means that the 50 units (50,000 tons) processed at Amsterdam will all have to be shipped *at least* 307 miles each, a total of $50 \times 307 = 15,350$ (in units of a thousand ton-miles), and the subsequent allocation will determine the extent to which this minimum will be exceeded. If we add 15,350 to the cost function, we may reduce all the cost elements in the first row of the matrix by 307.

Exercise 6.4

Simplify the second row (Barcelona) in Table 6.1 by the method just described.

How much must then be added to the cost function?

Reducing all the rows in this way gives Table 6.3.

TABLE 6.3

Plankton Allocation: First Stage in Matrix Reduction

| Factory | Market | | | | | Mileage Sub-tracted | Amount Deliv-ered | Product in ton-miles, to be added to cost function |
	M	P	R	S	T			
A	371	0	752	56	376	307	50	15,350
B	84	121	323	120	0	564	72	40,608
C	306	100	617	0	351	631	57	35,967
D	536	0	913	264	499	103	21	2,163
						Sub-total		94,088

The reduction ensures that the lowest cost in each of the rows is zero, and may now be carried a stage further by doing the same for the columns. Each of these contains a zero except M and R; the lowest entry in the former is 84. If we reduce all the entries in column M by this amount, we must increase the cost function by $84 \times 36 = 3024$; similarly, by subtracting 323 from all the entries in column 5 we add 11,305 to the cost function and arrive at the completely reduced matrix in Table 6.4 which has at least one zero in each row and column.

TABLE 6.4

Plankton Allocation: Final Stage in Matrix Reduction

Factory	Market						
	M	P	R	S	T		
A	287	0	429	56	376	Sub-total from previous	
B	0	121	0	120	0	reduction	94,088
C	222	100	294	0	351	Sub-total from this	
D	452	0	590	264	499	reduction	14,329
						Grand total	108,417
Mileage subtracted	84	0	323	0	0		
Amount delivered	36	69	35	20	40		
Product to be added to cost function	3,024	0	11,305	0	0	Sub-total	14,329

The figure 108,417 belongs to a useful class of estimates called 'lower bounds'. We know that, whatever the final allocation may be, it cannot possibly give a lower 'cost' than this – a valuable, though incomplete, piece of information in many problems.

We now combine Tables 6.2 and 6.4 into Table 6.5, where the reduced costs appear in the small rectangles within each cell, and the common-sense allocations are also entered, zero values being omitted. The row and column totals are included for checking.

TABLE 6.5

Plankton Allocation: Feasible Solution

Market	M	P	R	S	T
Totals	36	69	35	20	40
A 50	287 / **2**	0 / **48**	429	56	376
B 72	0 / **32**	121	0	120	0 / **40**
C 57	222 / **2**	100	294 / **35**	0 / **20**	351
D 21	452	0 / **21**	590	264	499

Table 6.6 shows how the 'fictitious costs' are calculated from cost elements for occupied cells. Column M has been arbitrarily chosen as the starting-point, and a cost element of zero entered at its foot. Taking the *occupied* cells in this column – those containing unencircled figures – we enter cost elements in the corresponding rows in such a way that the cost entry in any occupied cell is the sum of its corresponding row and column elements. Thus we have 287 as the cost element in the first row, and this in turn generates −287 at the bottom of the second column in order to add up to the zero in cell AP.

The fictitious costs for the unoccupied squares are then found by adding together the row and column cost elements: they are the encircled figures in Table 6.6. If none of the fictitious costs exceeds the true cost, the allocation as a whole has minimum cost.

There are two cells in Table 6.6 where this is not so; the

TABLE 6.6

Plankton Allocation: Calculation of Fictitious Costs

Factory	Market Totals	M 36	P 69	R 35	S 20	T 40	Fictitious Cost Element
A	50	[287] 2	[0] 48	[429] (359)	[56] (65)	[376] (287)	287
B	72	[0] 32	[121] (−287)	[0] (72)	[120] (−222)	[0] 40	0
C	57	[222] 2	[100] (−65)	[294] 35	[0] 20	[351] (222)	222
D	21	[452] (287)	[0] 21	[590] (359)	[264] (65)	[499] (287)	287
Fictitious Cost Element		0	−287	72	−222	0	

first is AS where the fictitious cost, 65, exceeds the true cost by 9. In cell BR, the fictitious cost exceeds the true cost by 72, an even greater difference. We therefore choose the latter, and cheapen the solution by allocating to it as great an amount as possible: it is marked with a plus sign in the left-hand part of Table 6.7. We now look along the row for an entry in a column which also contains at least one other occupied cell and mark it with a minus sign – in this case, cell BM with an entry of 32. Next we look down the same column for an entry in a row which also contains another occupied cell, and mark it with a plus sign. This goes on with alternate plus and minus signs until we eventually arrive back at cell BR: the route is shown in the left hand part of Table 6.7.

TABLE 6.7

Plankton Allocation: First Iteration

	M	P	R	S	T
A					
B	32−		+		
C	2+		35−		
D					

	M	P	R	S	T
A					
B			32		
C	34		3		
D					

TABLE 6.8

Plankton Allocation: Result of First Iteration

Factory	Market Totals	M	P	R	S	T	Fictitious Cost Element
		36	69	35	20	40	
A	50	287 **2** −	0 **48**	429 (359)	56 + (65)	376 (359)	287
B	72	0 (−72)	121 (−359)	0 **32**	120 (−294)	0 **40**	−72
C	57	222 **34** +	100 (−65)	294 **3**	0 **20** −	351 (294)	222
D	21	452 (287)	0 **21**	590 (359)	264 (65)	499 (359)	287
Fictitious Cost Element		0	−287	72	−222	72	

Having found the route, we move as large a number as possible into cell BR, adding and subtracting to preserve the factory and market totals. Negative allocations are meaningless, so the largest number in this case must be 32; it leads to a zero in cell BM as shown in the right-hand side of Table 6.7. The reduction in cost so obtained is $72 \times 32 = 2,304$ (which may readily be checked by comparing the total costs for Tables 6.6 and 6.8).

Table 6.8 shows the situation at the end of the first iteration, with the new fictitious costs. Cell AS still has an excess of fictitious over true cost of 9 units; the plus and minus signs show the route for adjustment, and Table 6.9 gives the result of

TABLE 6.9

Plankton Allocation: Optimum Solution

Factory	Market Totals	M 36	P 69	R 35	S 20	T 40	Fictitious Cost Element
A	50	287 (278)	0 48	429 (350)	56 2	376 (350)	278
B	72	0 (−72)	121 (−350)	0 32	120 (−294)	0 40	−72
C	57	222 36	100 (−56)	294 3	0 18	351 (294)	222
D	21	452 (278)	0 21	590 (350)	264 (56)	499 (350)	278
Fictitious Cost Element		0	−278	72	−222	72	

the second iteration, which is the optimum solution. Its overall cost is 8,986 units, which when added to the original minimum total obtained by reducing the matrix (108,417) gives a grand total of 117,403.

Exercise 6.5

What reduction in cost would you expect between Tables 6.8 and 6.9? Check your answer against the costs of these two allocations.

Exercise 6.6

What is the total cost of transportation given by the optimum solution? What is the saving over the original 'common-sense' solution of Table 6.2?

Exercise 6.7

The Assistant Transport Manager was also asked to produce a common-sense solution. He used almost the same method, except that he began with the biggest *factory* and allocated its output to the nearest markets. His result is tabulated below. Find the cost of this solution and use the method of fictitious costs to derive the optimum.

Factory	Milan	Paris	Rome	Centre Strasbourg	Turin	Total
Amsterdam	4	32	14			50
Barcelona	32				40	72
Copenhagen		37		20		57
Dieppe			21			21
Total	36	69	35	20	40	200

It is possible, as in the Simplex method, to calculate ranges of validity for the solution. For instance, in cell *AM* of Table 6.9, the fictitious cost is 9 units less than the true cost: it follows that a reduction in the true cost of up to 9 units will not affect the solution, but a change greater than this will. If a new Dutch motorway were to reduce the distance from Amsterdam to the Italian cities by 25 miles, the true costs in the cells for Amsterdam to Milan, Rome and Turin (Table 6.9) would fall to 262, 404 and 351 respectively. The fictitious cost for Amsterdam to Milan, cell AM, would then be greater than the true cost and Amsterdam would supply Milan rather than Strasbourg, with corresponding adjustments in the shipments from Copenhagen to those two centres.

The Plankton problem was such that the total productive and market capacities were exactly equal, but the transportation method may also be used for inequalities. An example can easily be constructed by supposing that the Turin centre and its market no longer exist, so that the total productive capacity exceeds the total demand by 20 units.

The problem can still be expressed in the same general form, with only a few changes. The column which previously represented the Turin outlet now becomes a disposal column. Each cell in it is given an artificially high cost, much greater than any other cost, which we shall call Z – this device ensures that all these cells will have the lowest priority. By altering Table 6.9 in this way, and using it as a first feasible solution, we arrive at the statement of the problem given in Table 6.10.

The occupied cell in column T is BT which contains 40 units; its cost in the original table was 0 and is now Z, so the cost of the solution as a whole becomes $8{,}968 + 40Z$. The corresponding fictitious costs are also shown in Table 6.10, and we can see that all the cells in column T now have fictitious costs greater than the actual ones, the greatest difference being in cell AT. By transferring the greatest possible number – two – into this cell, we arrive at Table 6.11, and two further iterations give Table 6.12, the optimum solution.

The first iteration decreased the cost by $2 \times 350 = 700$, the second by 1×294 and the third by 7,992, bringing the total cost in Table 6.12 to zero, which corresponds to the lower bound as described on page 142. The additional 'cost', $40Z$, is not counted because it was introduced as an artificial device for dealing with an inequality.

A similar device is used when the total manufacturing capacity is less than the total market: an extra row would be added, representing an imaginary additional factory with an output

TABLE 6.10

Plankton Allocation with Turin Excluded:
First Feasible Solution

Factory	Market Totals	M 36	P 69	R 35	S 20	T 40	Fictitious Cost Element
A	50	[287] (278)	[0] 48	[429] (350)	[56] 2 –	[Z] + (Z+350)	278
B	72	[0] (−72)	[121] (−350)	[0] 32 +	[120] (−294)	[Z] 40 –	−72
C	57	[222] 36	[100] (−56)	[294] 3 –	[0] 18 +	[Z] (Z+294)	222
D	21	[452] (278)	[0] 21	[590] (350)	[264] (56)	[Z] (Z+350)	278
Fictitious Cost Element		0	−278	72	−222	Z+72	

exactly equal to the deficiency in manufacturing capacity. All the cells in this row would have a 'penalty' cost of Z, and the resulting distribution plan would show which parts of the total market should be satisfied.

Using an artificial penalty cost to exclude certain sets of solutions is a convenient method which is widely used in cost-minimization problems; similarly, we may use zero or negative costs to impose priorities. Thus, if local politics made it necessary for Strasbourg to be supplied from a French source,

TABLE 6.11

Plankton Allocation with Turin Excluded:
Result of First Iteration

Factory	Market Totals	M 36	P 69	R 35	S 20	T 40	Fictitious Cost Element
A	50	287 / (−72)	0 / 48	429 / (0)	56 / (−294)	z / 2	−72
B	72	0 / (−72)	121 / (0)	0 / 34 +	120 / (−294) −	z / 38	−72
C	57	222 / 36 / (294)	100 / 1 −	294 / 1	0 / 20 +	z / (z+294)	222
D	21	452 / (−72)	0 / 21	590 / (0)	264 / (−294)	z	−72
Fictitious Cost Element		0	+72	72	−222	z+72	

a negative cost for cell DS would ensure that the full capacity
of the Dieppe factory was allocated to Strasbourg.

Exercise 6.8

Pythagoras Plankton have decided that plankton processed
in Amsterdam shall not be sold in the Italian market. How
would you represent this decision in the allocation problem,
and what would be its effect on the company's distribution
costs?

TABLE 6.12

Plankton Allocation with Turin Excluded:
Result of Second Iteration

Factory	Market Totals	M 36	P 69	R 35	S 20	T 40	Fictitious Cost Element
A	50	287 / ⓪	0 / 48	429 / ⓪	56 / ⓪	z / 2	0
B	72	0 / 36	121 / ⓪	0 / 35	120 / ⓪	z / 1	0
C	57	222 / ⓪	100 / ⓪	294 / ⓪	0 / 20	z / 37	0
D	21	452 / ⓪	0 / 21	590 / ⓪	264 / ⓪	z / ⓩ	0
Fictitious Cost Element		0	0	0	0	z	

WIDER USES OF THE TRANSPORTATION METHOD

The idea of transportation can be extended to cover not only physical movement but other changes of state with which costs are associated. One common group of applications considers various periods of time as the 'destinations' – as was done in the planning problem of Jones and Rope described in the

previous chapter – and may even use them as 'sources' as well.[47]
The next exercise shows how quite complex situations can be
described in terms of transportation.

Exercise 6.9

Clerk and Maxwell Ltd make a chemical compound,
3-blindmycin. The demand for this product is seasonal, and
the productive capacity allocated to it follows roughly the
seasonal trend. The sales forecast for 1970 is:

1st Quarter	60,000 mg.
2nd Quarter	97,000 mg.
3rd Quarter	118,000 mg.
4th Quarter	95,000 mg.
Total	370,000 mg.

The productive capacity allocated is:

1st Quarter	51,000 mg.
2nd Quarter	80,000 mg.
3rd Quarter	119,000 mg.
4th Quarter	100,000 mg.
Total	350,000 mg.

There is therefore a deficiency of 20,000 mg. in total productive capacity, and the company's usual practice is to make
this up by buying from an outside supplier at a price of £70
per 1,000 mg. The price is falling, however, and the Chief
Buyer estimates that it will fall at a uniform rate from £70 in
the first quarter to £67 in the last.

The internal production cost is £50 per 1,000 mg. and this
holds good as long as the chemical is sold in the same quarter
as it is produced. If it is sold in the following quarter, it incurs
a storage cost of £1 per 1,000 mg. If it is sold two quarters
afterwards, the storage cost goes up to £2, but there is an
additional cost of £10 for filtering and re-testing the material.
If it is sold three quarters afterwards, it must also be re-distilled
at a total extra cost (including storage charges) of £30 per
1,000 mg. For any further delay, the product must be scrapped.

If orders are held over for one quarter, the loss (in customer

	Sales Forecast / Productive Capacity	1st Quarter 60	2nd Quarter 97	3rd Quarter 118	4th Quarter 95
1st Quarter	51	50	51	62	80
2nd Quarter	80	55	50	51	62
3rd Quarter	119	59	55	50	51
4th Quarter	100	63	59	55	50
Buy Outside	20	70	69	68	67

Sales and Productive Capacity   Costs are given in
are in units of 1,000 mg.   £ per 1,000 mg.

goodwill and extra administration) is estimated at £5; for two quarters, £9 and for three quarters' delay, £13. Check that the above matrix is an adequate description of the problem, and find the optimum solution.

NON-INTUITIVE SOLUTIONS

The solution to Exercise 6.9 is an interesting example of a result which goes against our intuition. The Purchasing Department in procuring 3-blindmycin from outside sources, would almost certainly recommend intuitively that it be bought in the last quarter when it is cheapest, but the linear programming solution suggests otherwise.

Non-intuitive solutions of this sort will usually occur when either

(a) the problem has not been properly defined in the first instance, or

(b) the linear programming formulation expresses a broad view of the problem which cuts across departmental responsibilities.

An example of the first type is afforded by dietary problems. If we know the prices and nutritional factors for a range of foods and the minimum nutritional requirements for a family, we may set up a linear programming matrix which produces a mimimum-cost diet. This may well contain a ridiculously large proportion of potatoes because they are a cheap source of Vitamin C, and because the problem did not specify any maximum restrictions on individual foodstuffs. One exercise closely resembling the Fermat Furniture example was carried out in a chemical factory with similar results.[46] The solution indicated the manufacture of a product in quantities far above the most optimistic estimate of the total market. A maximum as well as a minimum sales figure had to be specified, and the whole pricing policy was called into question as a result.

Examples of the second type tend to occur in fairly large matrices, when the data are obtained from a variety of origins. The individual managers within the several departments tend to organize work so that the department itself is at maximum efficiency (technically called 'sub-optimization') whereas maximum *overall* efficiency may conflict with this. Suppose a shop in a motor-car factory is making pistons and has some spare capacity. Increasing the output of pistons will lower their unit cost, but will produce a useless excess if it is not accompanied by a corresponding increase in the number of cylinder blocks.

The linear programming solution may also suggest methods of working. Newby and Deam found in scheduling an oil refinery that

The optimum blends as determined by the computer were in some cases considerably different from current practice. These blends were physically checked in the laboratory and found to agree with the properties as formulated by the solution and to meet appropriate specification requirements.[39]

Thus linear programming may not only solve our current problems but may contribute to our insight of the whole business of being managers. One industrial statistician has summed up in these words: 'Unless my solution generates at least four new problems, I consider that I have failed'.

6

Solutions to Exercises

Exercise 6.1

(a) $2,000 \times 32 \times 648$ shillings $= 41,472,000$ shillings
$$= £2,073,600$$

(b) Nil, because no allocation has been made under this heading

Exercise 6.2

Yes, because the cost of transportation per mile is the same throughout.

Exercise 6.3

Working in units of one thousand tons, we have:

$$
\begin{array}{rcr}
2 \times 678 = & & 1,356 \\
48 \times 307 = & & 14,736 \\
32 \times 648 = & & 20,736 \\
40 \times 564 = & & 22,560 \\
2 \times 937 = & & 1,874 \\
35 \times 1,248 = & & 43,680 \\
20 \times 631 = & & 12,620 \\
21 \times 103 = & & 2,163 \\
\hline
\text{Total} & & 119,725
\end{array}
$$

Exercise 6.4

Lowest mileage 564 (Barcelona to Turin)

New row:	M	P	R	S	T
	84	121	323	120	0

Total amount from Barcelona $= 72$ thousand tons (Table 6.2)
Amount to be added to cost function $= 564 \times 72 = £40,608$

Exercise 6.5

The difference between fictitious and true costs in cell *AS* was 9, and 2 units were moved into it. The saving would be $9 \times 2 = 18$ units. Each unit represents 1,000 tons making an out-and-return journey of 2 miles at one shilling per mile, giving a cost per unit of £100 – the monetary saving is therefore £1,800.

Check.

Total from Table 6.8 =	9,004 units	
,, ,, ,, 6.9 =	8,986 ,,	
Difference	18 units	

Exercise 6.6

'Lower bound' cost =	108,417 units
Optimum additional cost =	8,986 ,,
Total cost =	117,403 units
=	£11,740,300
Cost of 'common-sense' solution =	£11,972,500
Saving =	£232,200
Saving as percentage of original total =	1·94%

Exercise 6.7

The cost of this solution is £13,166,100.
The optimum solution is as shown in Table 6.9.

Exercise 6.8

Enter a penalty cost *Z* in cells *AM*, *AR* and *AT*. Since these cells are unoccupied in Table 6.9, the original solution would not be changed and so the distribution costs would not be affected.

Exercise 6.9

	Sales Forecast / Productive Capacity	1st Quarter 60	2nd Quarter 97	3rd Quarter 118	4th Quarter 95
1st Quarter	51	50 / **51**	51	62	80
2nd Quarter	80	55	50 / **80**	51	62
3rd Quarter	119	59	55 / **1**	50 / **118**	51
4th Quarter	100	63	59 / **5**	55	50 / **95**
Buy Outside	20	70 / **9**	69 / **11**	68	67

NOTES AND REFERENCES

46 Battersby, A., *Linear Programming in a Small Batch Chemical Plant*. Paper delivered to the Manchester Branch of the Institution of Chemical Engineers, December 1962.
47 Magee, J. F., *Production Planning and Inventory Control* (McGraw-Hill, 1958), p. 146.

More information about 3-blindmycin will be found in:
Comfort, A., *Come Out to Play* (Eyre & Spottiswoode, 1961).

7
Simulation by Symbols

The little actor cons another part.
Filling from time to time his 'humorous stage'
With all the Persons, down to palsied Age,
That life brings with her in her equipage;
    As if his whole vocation
    Were endless imitation.

WORDSWORTH, *Ode on Intimations of Immortality*

THE study of computers will show us how close is the connexion between the 'new' mathematics of the business world and the systematic studies of logical relationships which originated with Aristotle. This association is evident in the study of business systems by the method known as 'simulation'. As its name implies, simulation enables a manager to study the system which he controls by imitating or 'simulating' its behaviour. As examples of simulation in its widest sense, we have:

1. A model in a wind-tunnel test, for deducing the aerodynamic behaviour of a new type of aircraft.

2. The 'flight simulator' used for training airline pilots; this is a full-scale representation of a flight-deck, which responds to the pilot's handling of the controls in the same way as a real air liner.

3. The mechanical 'tortoises', Elmer and Elsie, built by Dr W. Gray Walter. They illustrate the nervous system of an animal, building up astonishingly lifelike behaviour from the interactions of simple electrical circuits.

These are all physical models with the common characteristic of reproducing the *behaviour* of the real object which they represent. In theory, the behaviour of any system can be deduced in all circumstances provided that its structure is completely known: given the exact shape, surface characteristics and speed of a supersonic aircraft, we ought to be able to compute the nature of the shock wave, but the calculation would be so laborious and liable to error that the 'simulation' in a wind-tunnel is cheaper and more convenient.

A simulation model need not be mechanical; the diagram in Figure 7.1 is a rather frivolous example of an *abstract* model. It represents the game of Snakes and Ladders. There is, for example, a snake with its head on square 16 and its tail on square 4; there is a ladder from square 2 to square 62.

Throwing the die is represented by 'Select a number at random from 1 to 6 inclusive'. See how precisely the rules have been designed: if you throw a six, and have a second throw, do you go down a snake if the six alone lands you on its head? These rules show clearly that you do not. Notice also that the rules for finishing the game have been carefully defined.

Exercise 7.1

Is any skill involved in the game of Snakes and Ladders?

PROBLEMS OF ORGANIZATIONS

How does all this affect the executive who is concerned with the more serious problems of controlling some sort of *organization*? There is a fundamental resemblance between his problem and that of the aircraft designer: the manager, like the designer, knows the *structure* of what he is dealing with, but its complexity prevents him from deducing its behaviour. Consequently, he is obliged to make decisions of which the effect can be only imperfectly predicted.

CONTROL LOOPS

Imperfect decisions of this sort mean that the manager is experimenting with the business itself – making changes, observing the results and modifying his instructions accordingly. He has set up a 'feedback control loop' between himself and

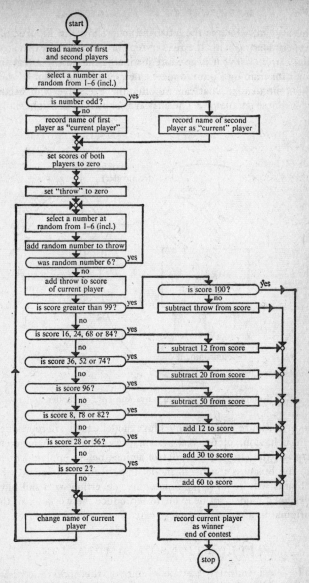

Fig. 7.1 Simulation of a contest: logical flow diagram

the system, which is the left-hand loop shown in Figure 7.2. Experimenting with the real system in this way is expensive and can be risky; it is no more justifiable than using a real air liner for training a pilot to meet emergencies. The pilot has his flight simulator: what can we offer the executive who needs a 'business simulator'? The answer is shown in the right-hand

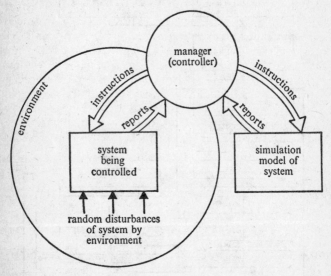

Fig. 7.2 Relationship of system, environment, controller and mode

loop of Figure 7.2. By giving him a model which will reproduce the behaviour of the real system, we enable the manager to try out the effect of his control actions before applying them to the business itself. No model is perfect, so the answer he obtains will be an approximate one; nevertheless, a skilfully-designed model can be made to reproduce the workings of the original to a remarkably close extent.

APPLICATIONS OF SIMULATION

The steel industry has been one of the most successful industrial exploiters of simulation models; one of the earliest papers is a very readable description of a problem in a melting shop,[48] and the B.I.S.R.A. Annual Report for 1961 mentions a similar problem (p. 84). Planning the work of soaking pits at the Abbey Works of the Steel Company of Wales has been improved with the help of a simulation model[49]; the unloading of iron ore at Ijmuiden has also been studied.[50] A recent paper dealing with steel fabrication showed that an extra crane costing £15,000 would not be needed in a new materials-handling system.[51] A rather unusual study investigated the effect of weather on production scheduling for sugar-beet factories in the U.S.A.[52] Pit-haulage in France [53] and the method of warning miners in a colliery[54] have also been simulated, as well as a wide variety of traffic and transport problems.[55,56] Much of the simulation work in the military field is kept secret, but occasionally some information dribbles out; a paper from the United States Air Force[57] describes a case in which direct experimentation on the system would be undesirable, to say the least – simulating 'a large-scale two-sided global war'. Could simulation do more?

DEFINING THE SYSTEM

In order to build a model we must break down the system into its component parts, but before doing this we need to say more precisely what we mean by a 'system'. This word has been used so far to mean 'that which is being controlled', and we cannot hope to define it more exactly until we have examined the range of control actions which is to be studied.

To make this rather abstract point clearer, consider a transport company whose operations we wish to study by building a model. It consists of a fleet of lorries operating from a central warehouse; do these physical components, then, make up the whole system? If all we wish to observe is the effect of different speeds or scheduling procedures, then the answer is probably yes. If, however, we are concerned with the desirability of opening a new warehouse or adding more lorries to the fleet, we must include those *potential* components in the system; if we wish to observe the effects of our actions on the service to customers, then the customers themselves must be represented in some way.

BOUNDARIES

In short, the system is defined by a *boundary* which we draw around it. Everything inside the boundary is 'the system'; everything that lies outside constitutes 'the environment' in which the system operates. Drawing this boundary correctly is difficult: some day, perhaps, operational researchers may discover 'cleavage planes' between a system and its environment, and use them to separate the system as a lapidary cuts his gems. In the meantime, the best definition of a boundary remains a matter for individual judgement – a part of the *art* of simulation, as distinct from the more methodical procedures to be mentioned later.

ANALYSING THE SYSTEM

Suppose we have decided that our system is to contain so many warehouses, lorries and customers' unloading bays; then the next question to be answered is, 'How much detail must we include?' Obviously, a highly detailed model will reproduce the real system more faithfully, but it will also tend to be cumbersome and clumsy. On the other hand, a very rough model will cover a narrower range of activities and give answers with a wider margin of error. Should we, for example, consider each driver to be an integral part of his vehicle or not? Here again we are faced with deciding just what sorts of questions we want the model to deal with. If the driver and the vehicle are to all intents inseparable in real life, then it is pointless to separate them in the model. If, on the other hand, we want to know what will happen if we run our vehicles on two shifts from a pool of drivers, the drivers will have to be represented as separate entities.

In this way we shall arrive at a list of all the physical

components which help to make up the system. Our imaginary transport company might well yield the following list:

Central Warehouse
with two existing bays for loading and up to three possible extra ones.

Five Lorries
and up to three possible extra ones.

Ten Destinations
each with one unloading bay.

STATES OF THE COMPONENTS

Writing down a description of a real process is never an easy job; one is faced with what at first appears to be a chaotic jumble of men and machines. In order to unravel the separate threads of activity, the investigator needs a methodical procedure. Work study, for instance, has given us the flow process chart, the multiple activity chart and so on. These can be helpful, although they are not sufficient in themselves; a more specialized procedure is needed for a simulation. One widely-used method is to list the 'states' of each component and then to discover the rules which govern changes from one state to another.

To take a simple example, our loading bays can be 'Vacant' or 'Occupied', which we call State 1 and State 0 respectively. The lorries, however, can exist in any one of five states.

State 1 = At warehouse, waiting to load.
State 2 = At loading bay, taking on load.
State 3 = Full, moving from loading bay to destination.
State 4 = At destination, unloading.
State 5 = Empty, moving from destination to warehouse.

The possible transitions between these five states are very restricted. They are shown in Figure 7.3.

We shall use this diagram to build up a simulation routine, but it should be pointed out that in practice we should almost

Fig. 7.3 States of the components of a system

certainly need a wider range of states and transitions, as exemplified by Figure 7.4. The 'non-existent' state which this shows (State 0) is a useful device when we are dealing with an

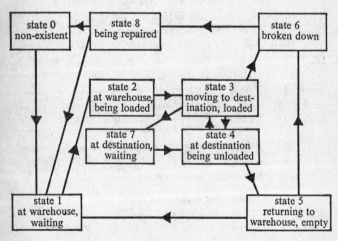

Fig. 7.4 A more complicated set of lorry states

expanding business and want to bring in new vehicles during a simulated period of operation. Another big difference from Figure 7.3 is that *alternative* transitions are possible: a vehicle may go from State 3 to any of States 4, 6 or 7.

Some builders of simulation models would prefer to put Figure 7.4 into a different form – a table or 'matrix' of possible transitions; Figure 7.5 shows the diagram from Figure 7.4 expressed in this alternative way. The entry '1' means that the

		second state								
		0	1	2	3	4	5	6	7	8
first state	0	1	1	0	0	0	0	0	0	0
	1	0	1	1	0	0	0	0	0	0
	2	0	0	1	1	0	0	0	0	0
	3	0	0	0	1	1	0	1	1	0
	4	0	0	0	1	1	1	0	0	0
	5	0	1	0	0	0	1	1	0	0
	6	0	0	0	0	0	0	1	0	1
	7	0	0	0	0	1	0	0	1	0
	8	1	1	0	0	0	0	0	0	1

Fig. 7.5 Matrix corresponding to Figure 7.4

transition is possible, whereas '0' shows it to be impossible. A brief study will show that Figures 7.4 and 7.5 do in fact represent the same set of connexions between states.

Finally, returning to Figure 7.3, we can see that this abstract diagram is a general one and could be used to represent not only a lorry, but also a goods train, a ship, an aircraft or even a man with a wheelbarrow.

Exercise 7.2

Draw up a list of states which would adequately describe some repetitive process with which you are familiar. Possible examples are:

(a) Wallpapering a room.
(b) Answering a mixed pile of correspondence.
(c) Mowing a lawn.
(d) The work of a barber's shop.

CLOCKS

The components of the system have been selected, their states defined and their possible transitions listed; what is the next step? Obviously we must now find out the *rules* which govern the transitions. One simple and common rule is that a transition from one state to another occurs purely because time has elapsed. The simulation therefore needs a *clock*, which is no more than a simple counter, to govern its changes.

There is no reason why the time kept by the clock should be the same as time in the real world – indeed, there is good reason why it should not. One of the objects of a simulation is to accumulate experience at a much faster rate than is possible in real life, so our 'simulated time' will usually pass more quickly than natural time.

The clock in our model will go on counting up seconds, minutes, hours or days until it reaches some pre-set figure at which it stops the simulation run, itself included, like the time switch on an electric cooker.

How long should each 'tick' be? We have met a similar question before, in considering the physical components of the system: essentially it can be reduced to 'How much detail do we want the model to include?' Here again we must strike a balance between precision and practicability: simulating the flow of neutrons in a nuclear reactor may call for a 'tick' of a millionth of a second, but in an industrial model such as our transport company we are more likely to need a unit of several minutes or even an hour. The decision rests with the simulator – he is free to choose a time unit as long or as short as he pleases, knowing that the longer the unit, the faster but cruder his simulation will be.

TRANSITIONS OF STATE

Let us look at a specific transition in Figure 7.3 – from State 4 to State 5. Suppose that in real life a lorry is always unloaded in one hour, and that we have chosen an hour as our 'tick', or unit of time. The transition rule is a simple one: 'A lorry in State 4 automatically passes to State 5 in the next time period'. In terms of the flow diagram in Figure 7.1, the same rule can be expressed as follows:

Advance clock by one unit.
Was lorry in State 4?
If the answer is yes, change the state of the lorry to 5.

When the lorry reaches State 5, we must know the cir-cumstance in which it will pass to State 1. This obviously depends on the duration of the return journey – say, 3 hours. One convenient way of effecting the transition is to put a counter in the lorry which can be set to three hours and which will count down as the clock ticks away. The rule for the next transition is then, 'If the lorry is in State 5 and its counter registers zero, then change its State to 1'. This rule may be condensed into a mathematical notation such as

$$L\,5 \to 1, \qquad C = 0 \qquad\qquad (7.1)$$

(reading L as 'Lorry State' $\to$ as 'becomes' and the comma as 'if').

RANDOM EFFECTS

Sometimes we cannot say definitely whether a lorry will take 2, 3 or 4 hours for the return journey, because the time varies randomly between these three values. Then before we can set the counter on our lorry we must know the relative frequencies of these periods in real life; suppose they were:

> 2 hours: 25% of the journeys
> 3 hours: 50% ,, ,, ,,
> 4 hours: 25% ,, ,, ,,

This simple frequency distribution is easy to simulate. Whenever we wish to set the counter for a return journey we may toss two coins and use the rule –

For 2 heads, take 2 hours:
For a head and a tail, take 3 hours:
For 2 tails, take 4 hours,

– because a head and a tail together will occur twice as fre-quently as either two heads or two tails.

In this way, we make a random selection from a frequency distribution. Simulations are especially useful when many random factors have to be considered, and a good deal of the research into the subject is devoted to the methods of generating random numbers and reproducing frequency distributions. The methods which are used may be grouped into two main classes: first, truly random numbers may be taken from a table; secondly, a device like 'Ernie' (Electronic Random Number Indicating Equipment) may be used. Both are rather clumsy; for convenience, genuinely random numbers are replaced by 'pseudo-random' numbers; these are generated by fairly simple calculations which are known to produce strings of numbers indistinguishable in the short run from truly random ones.

Typical of these calculations is the 'mid-square' method, in which a large number is squared and its middle digits taken as a random sequence. They in turn are squared and produce the next sequence: Tocher[65] quotes the following example:

$$76^2 = 5776$$
$$77^2 = 5929$$
$$92^2 = 8464$$
$$46^2 = 2116$$
$$11^2 = 0121$$
$$12^2 = 0144 \quad \text{etc.}$$

This method, due to Von Neumann, is by no means infallible, as the following sequence shows:

$$84^2 = 7056$$
$$05^2 = 0025$$
$$02^2 = 0004$$
$$00^2 = 0000$$
$$00^2 = 0000$$

There seems little point in striving too earnestly after perfection in this matter, since eminent mathematicians themselves have been known to disagree on the question of what 'truly random' means.

The frequency distribution quoted above is much simpler than any we should meet in reality. One is more likely to find the journey times distributed in a less tidy way – for example,

Journey Time	Frequency	Random Numbers Allocated
1 hour	nil	
2 hours	23%	01–23
3 hours	36%	24–59
4 hours	29%	60–88
5 hours	11%	89–99
6 hours	1%	00
Total	100%	

Then to obtain the time for any single journey we pick a random number from the range 1 to 100 inclusive and look up the corresponding journey time in the table.

If the frequency distribution can be fitted to one of the known statistical patterns, (e.g. Gaussian or Poisson), the time for a single journey can be calculated mathematically from a random number without the need for a tabulated list of values. For simulations on an electronic computer, sub-routines which will generate pseudo-random numbers and derive statistics from standard frequency distributions are usually preferred to those which use tables, because they make less demands on the limited storage capacity of the machine.

A roulette wheel is a simple mechanical method of producing a string of random numbers, and consequently this part of the simulation process is often referred to as 'the Monte Carlo method'. The same phrase is sometimes used for describing an entire simulation in which random effects are introduced, and is therefore ambiguous.

CONDITIONAL TRANSITIONS

The transition from State 1 to State 2 differs from those already discussed, in that it depends upon the states of the loading bays. If all of these are occupied, then, obviously, no more lorries can pass from State 1 to State 2 until a bay becomes free.

Conditions such as this one link the various components

together, and to enumerate them completely calls for careful logical analysis. If a computer is to be used, then even such elementary rules as 'No two bodies can occupy the same space at the same time' must be explicitly stated, otherwise the mis-named 'electronic brain' will overlook them. In fact, the time spent on conventional mathematics in the average industrial simulation is likely to be small in comparison with that devoted to logic.

Exercise 7.3

If 'State 0' means 'Occupied' when applied to a loading bay, can you think of a simple test which would tell whether *any* bay was free? (Try addition.)

TRANSITION PROBABILITIES

How often does a lorry break down? In our imaginary transport company, only rarely – once in every thousand deliveries, let us say. If we wish to include breakdowns in our simulation, as in Figure 7.4, then we must arrange for the transition from State 3 to State 6 to have a probability of 0·001. Each time a vehicle is in State 3, a random number from 1 to 1,000 is selected: if it happens to be 1,000, the next transition will be to State 6 instead of State 7 or State 4.

TIME-CONTROLLED TRANSITIONS

When listing the physical components of the system, we took into account certain vehicles which might be added to the system during a simulated period of operation; similarly, they could be removed from the system. Changes of this sort would take place at times which were specified beforehand; an 'un-born' lorry would carry a 'date of birth' as part of its specifica-tion, and the transition from State 0 to State 1 would take place when the clock reached this date.

CRITERION OF PERFORMANCE

There can be no point at all in simulating a system unless we measure its performance in some way. In other words, the right hand control loop in Figure 7.2 must be closed with a 'feed-back' to the controller.

The criterion of performance will usually be some measure of cost or profit: indeed, Figure 7.2 suggests that it will correspond to the returns which the executive receives from the real-life system.

For the sake of simplicity, we may choose to use a measure such as 'idle machine-hours', on the grounds that a reduction in idleness will automatically bring down operating costs. These are only valid for the simplest models; when several diverse activities take place in the simulation, measurement in terms of money is the only way of reducing them to a common unit.

A SIMPLE EXAMPLE

In order to show how all these parts are assembled into a complete model let us consider the imaginary case of the Fetter Lane Transport Company. It has a central warehouse with two loading bays, and five lorries which run continuously to various destinations. The average time for an outward journey is 2 hours 50 minutes; for a return journey it is 2 hours 40 minutes. These times are not constant: they vary in a random manner as follows:

| Time of Journey | Percentage of Occasions | |
	Outward	Inward
	(State 3)	(State 5)
2 hours	33⅓%	50%
3 hours	50%	33⅓%
4 hours	16⅔%	16⅔%

Loading at the warehouse takes 2 hours and unloading at the destination takes 1 hour. After returning to the warehouse, each lorry must wait at least 1 hour for service and paper work, and may have to wait longer if there is no loading bay vacant.

The complete cycle of operations can therefore be represented by Figure 7.3; the expected time for a return trip is $9\frac{1}{2}$ hours, made up of:

Waiting	(State 1)	1 hour
Loading	(State 2)	2 hours
Delivering	(State 3)	2 hours 50 minutes
Unloading	(State 4)	1 hour
Returning	(State 5)	2 hours 40 minutes
	Total	9 hours 30 minutes

Each lorry spends less than a quarter of its total journey time at a loading bay, so one bay should be adequate to deal with four lorries if they arrive in a steady stream. However, variations in the journey times sometimes cause lorries to 'bunch' together so that they have to wait for a loading bay to fall vacant.

These delays are not serious at present, but the company proposes to buy three more lorries to deal with increasing business. The congestion at the bays will obviously get worse: how serious will it be? Would it be bad enough to justify a third loading bay?

The flowsheet for the simulation model is shown in Figure 7.6. The criterion of performance is the pattern of delays suffered by the lorries, and we have arranged to count the number of delays of 1 hour each, the number lasting 2 hours and so on. These numbers are to be stored in a set of 'delay registers' which are set to zero at first (Box 1) and increased (Box 18) whenever a lorry which has been delayed moves to the loading bay.

The 'tick' of the master clock is one hour. Each simulated lorry is given its own private clock, called the 'counter', which is arranged to count down to zero. When the counter reaches zero, the lorry moves to the next state unless it happens to be in State 1 and no loading bay is available: it must then wait, and the delay is registered as a negative number on the counter.

Fig. 7.6 Simulation flowsheet for the Fetter Lane Transport Company

The rest of the flowsheet is not difficult to follow; the sub-routine in Box 24 uses the throw of a die to select the journey times for States 3 and 5; Figure 7.7 gives it in detail.

Fig. 7.7 Sub-routine for setting counters

The routine shown in Figures 7.6 and 7.7 is interesting in two ways. First, it can deal with any number of lorries and any number of bays without modification. Secondly, it leaves nothing to imagination or common-sense, and can therefore be used as the basis for a computer programme, as is explained in the next chapter. It can also be used to 'programme' or teach a human being: you will find that if you work your way through the routine it will not be long before you start skipping odd steps here and there. It only needs about a hundred simulated time periods to impress the whole routine on your memory.

INPUT DATA

In order to start the model working, we must describe the current states of the components, as shown in the first column of Figure 7.8. Here we are simulating the existing fleet of five

lorry no.	100 input	clock settings											
		99	98	97	96	95	94	93	92	91	2	1	0
1 state	5	1	2		3			4	5		5		
counter	0	1	2	0	3	1	0	1	2	0	1		0
counter		0	1		2			0	1				
bay			1										
2 state	2		3		4	5		1	2		4	5	
counter	1	0	2	0	1	2	0	1	2	0	5	3	2
counter			1		0	1		0	1	2	0		
bay	2												
3 state	3		4	5				1	2		2	2	
counter	1	0	1	3	1	0	1	2	0	3	2	1	0
counter			0	2			0	1	1	3	2		
bay									1	2	2		
4 state	3	2	1	0		4	5		1		2	5	2
counter	3				1	2	0	1	0	−1	1	2	0
counter					0	1			0		2	1	
bay											1		
5 state	2	3					4	5		1	3	2	
counter	0	4	2	1	0	1	3	2	1	0	2	1	0
counter		3				0	2	1	0		1		
bay	1												
loading bay no.													
1 state	2	1	2		1			2		1	1		
state									1	2			
2 state	2		1						2		2		
state													
delay registers													
−1	0									1			6
−2	0												2
−3	0												0
−4	0												0
−5	0												0

Fig. 7.8 Results of simulation

lorries; No. 1 will complete its return journey in the next hour; No. 2 is loading at the second bay and No. 5 is about to finish loading at the first; Nos. 3 and 4 are on the outward journey.

Both loading bays are occupied, and the master clock is set so that the model will stop after it has simulated 100 hours' working.

The first delay occurs in the eighth hour (column 92) and affects lorry No. 4. By the time the run has ended, six delays of one hour and two of two hours have been registered. If the simulated delays agree with those observed in the real system, we are justified in assuming that the model is good enough for our needs, and using it as a basis for experimentation.

EXPERIMENTING WITH THE MODEL

Putting another three lorries into the model is very simple: we simply add their descriptions to the input data and repeat the simulation run.

With eight lorries, for instance, we get the following comparison:

| Number of delays of | 5 lorries | | 8 lorries | |
	2 bays	3 bays	2 bays	3 bays
1 hour	6	0	25	0
2 hours	2	0	5	0
More than 2 hours	0	0	0	0

These results, being derived from random numbers, are themselves liable to random variations, and the prudent experimenter will carry out several runs for each combination of bays and lorries, and apply statistical tests of significance to his results. If the runs are to yield the greatest possible amount of information, they should be arranged according to modern principles of experimental design.[58]

The model described above has been purposely kept simple, but in fact a very similar routine has been used by a large distributor of petroleum products as an aid to designing the loading points in a depot.

EXTENSIONS OF THE MODEL

Sometimes the first definition of a model turns out to be inadequate, because one cannot always assess the problems perfectly in the first place: this follows the scientific tradition, in which one experiment may point the way to the next.

If we study the working of which Figure 7.8 is a summary, we find that as many as three lorries may be in State 4 (unloading at destination) simultaneously. An observation like this may well lead us to ask, 'Have we been too vague about the destinations? Should we identify them as separate components and take account of possible delays there as well?' Such questions may lead us to extend the model into a more detailed form.

OTHER METHODS

The method used for building the model of the Fetter Lane Transport Company is only one of several which are available. It was appropriate to this example because at least one 'event' or change of state occurs in each time period. When the 'tick' of the master clock is short compared with the journey times, it may be more appropriate to jump forward by the amount shown on the lowest counter – that is to say, to the next event. We may go further and include the next event but one, and so on, so that we find ourselves *sorting* the lorries into the order of their counters.

This and other problems of model-building are discussed in a survey by Conway and others,[59] Harling,[60] Youle and others[61] and Tocher.[62] A bibliography of papers has also been compiled by Malcolm[63]; it is significant that of the 94 papers on industrial simulation listed in it, only 4 were published before 1954.

HUMAN DECISIONS IN SIMULATION

Sometimes a system we want to simulate contains human beings who inject decisions based on judgement. How can we incorporate them into our model?

An investigation may show that the allegedly 'inspired' decisions can be reduced to a set of logical rules or replaced by an optimizing technique such as linear programming. It is not uncommon for the scientific analysis of the system to show up its present inadequacies, and suggest means of overcoming them before the model is even built. (A similar phenomenon has been observed in computer feasibility studies.)

Alternatively, we may acknowledge the impossibility of rationalizing the decisions and stop the simulation run each time one is required. Then the model will supply the data on which the decision is based; after it has been made, the results are fed in as a fresh set of input data and the run is resumed. A typical example is in preparing a machine-loading programme or a delivery schedule for vehicles.

MANAGEMENT GAMES

We have already seen that a model can provide a means of experimenting with decisions and learning by mistakes. This forms the basis of management games, in which human beings are made to play major parts in a simulated business organization. Management games have become a subject in their own right, and can only be given a passing mention here.

THE ROLE OF COMPUTERS IN SIMULATION

A computer is not a prerequisite for a simulation model: much of the work quoted in the literature has been done with no more equipment than pencil and paper. Nevertheless, this type of work lends itself very readily to electronic computation, because it comprises a number of repetitive 'loops' of instructions, controlled by simple 'yes-no' decisions.

The high speed of an electronic computer allows us to accumulate 'experience' with the model much more quickly than in real life. For example, the British Petroleum Company have used their 'Mercury' computer to investigate the distribution of petrol and fuel oil in Belgium. One year's operations can be simulated in great detail in rather less than an hour, and the results are printed out as estimates of monthly operating costs. The effects of seasonal variations in demand have been analysed; so have the economics of changing the constitution of the barge fleet and providing additional storage at selected points. In effect, the simulation sorts out the possibilities of new capital investment according to their profitability; it also predicts the cost savings which will accrue from alterations in the day-to-day running of the business.

Some teams of investigators, including those at B.I.S.R.A. and the United Steel Company, have developed general simulation programmes for computers; these are essentially ways of describing the system in a methodical layout, which the computer itself can interpret into its own 'language' of instructions. The question of applying computers will be dealt with at greater length in the next chapter.

SIMULATION AND ANALYSIS

The problem of the Fetter Lane Transport Company, as laid out in Figure 7.3, could have been solved analytically by using a branch of mathematical statistics called the 'theory of queues'. One of the criticisms directed at people who build simulation models is that they are lazy men looking for some way of avoiding the mathematical analysis which would give them a more elegant, more general and ultimately quicker means of disposing of their problems.

And therefore a general custom of simulation is a vice, rising either of a natural falseness or fearfulness, or of a mind that hath some main faults, which because a man must needs disguise, it making him practise simulation in other things, lest his hand should be out of use.[64]

Such criticism is rarely justified, because very few practical situations can be effectively reduced to such simple terms. Nevertheless, the process of building a simulation model is essentially a simple one, calling for clear thought rather than mathematical sophistication.

The far-sighted manager, confronted with a complex problem in his own business, would do well to ask himself, 'Can simulation help me?' He may be surprised to find out how often the answer is 'Yes'. In fact, with Cambridge research workers helping 'Neddy' with a model of the entire national economy, we may find our business affected by a computer simulation whether we like it or not.

INDUSTRIAL DYNAMICS

A group of research workers at the Massachusetts Institute of Technology under Forrester[66] is investigating some of the problems of very large business organizations with the aid of a

Fig. 7.9 The encircled figures give the time in weeks needed for the transfer or processing of goods and documents

simulation programme called 'Dynamo'. They call this study *Industrial Dynamics* and have tended to concentrate on systems which are made up of chains such as factory–warehouse–distributor–retailer, (Figure 7.9) in which the relevant variables are either 'levels' or 'flows' controlled by managerial decisions at specified points. The simple flow diagram in Figure 7.9 is analysed into elements which contain these three factors: Figure 7.10 shows the first stage of the analysis. In

Fig. 7.10 Industrial Dynamics – Block Diagram

this diagram, the rectangle on the right shows unfulfilled orders and defines the mathematical symbol used to represent them, *UOR*, a coded reference number and an indication that this is a *level* (*L*).

Requisitions Received from Retail (*RRR*) add to this level, as the plus sign shows, and Shipments Sent from Retail (*SSR*) subtract from it: both these are *rates*. The functional relationship between the variables is expressed as an equation.

$$UOR.K = UOR.\mathcal{J} + (DT)(RRR.\mathcal{J}K - SSR.\mathcal{J}K)$$

This is read as 'The Unfulfilled Orders at Retail at time *K*

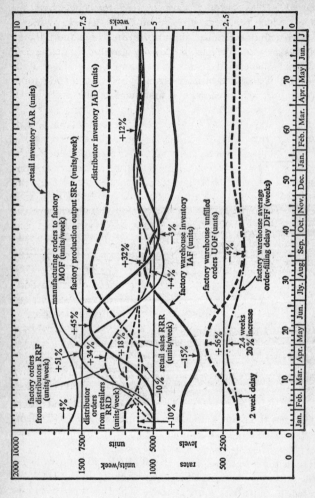

Fig. 7.11 Industrial Dynamics — Response Curves

equal the Unfulfilled Orders at Retail at time J plus an adjust-ment term. The adjustment term is the difference between the rate at which Requisitions Received from Retail flow in be-tween times J and K and the rate at which Shipments Sent from Retail flow out, multiplied by the time interval DT between J and K.'

The whole structure of a production-distribution system may be built up in this way as a set of 73 equations which constitute a mathematical model of it. They are, in effect, written in an 'autocode' language which the Dynamo simula-tion programme will accept. The desired input, consisting of a set of starting conditions and specified pattern of sales (RRR) may then be fed in and the behaviour pattern studied. In one simulation, a sudden 10% increase in an otherwise steady rate of sales produced the response shown in Figure 7.11. Fifteen weeks after the sales increased, the rate of production at the factory had surged up to an increase of 45%; forty weeks later it had swung back in an over-correction, and only after about seventy weeks could it be considered to have completely adjusted itself to the new rate of sales.

Forrester has shown that violent oscillations of this sort can occur in organizations with a chain structure, even though the individual links in the chain may be managed according to rational rules. Since such chains occur in the national economy (Figure 7.12) which is known to have a boom–slump cycle, the potential importance of industrial dynamics is self-evident. One has only to read 'sales of motor-cars' for 'retailers' and 'the steel industry' for 'factory' to see how Britain's recent economic history might be explained, and its future pro-ductivity improved, by the application of industrial dynamics.

Customers for motor-cars

	Garage	
Flow	Distributor	Flow
of	Motor manufacturer	of
orders	Body manufacturer	steel
	Sheet steel rolling mills	
	Steel producers	
	Imports of iron ore	

Fig. 7.12

7
Solutions to Exercises

Exercise 7.1

No, because the game has been completely defined by a logical flowsheet which calls for no human decision to be made.

Exercise 7.2

Are you quite sure that you have not tried to get too much detail into your diagram?

Exercise 7.3

Add all the state numbers together. If the answer is zero, all the bays must be occupied; if it is not zero, at least one bay is vacant.

NOTES AND REFERENCES

48 Jones, H. G., and Lee, A. M., 'Monte Carlo Methods in Heavy Industry', *Operational Research Quarterly* (September 1955) p. 108.

49 Thomas, G. W., Ramm, R. Q., and Rees, H. M., *Track Times and Soaking Pits*, Proceedings of the Second International Conference on Operational Research (1960), p. 336.

50 Lombaers, H. J. M., *Determining the One-Unloading Capacity of a Harbour Installation by Simulation on a Computer*, Proceedings of the Second International Conference on Operational Research (1960), p. 328.

51 McKee, P. R., Robinson, F. D., and Swan, A. W., 'An Investigation into the Materials Handling System of a Fabrication Works', *Operational Research Quarterly* (June 1962), p. 145.

52 Moody, L. A., *Production Allocation in the Beet Sugar Industry*, Proceedings of the Second International Conference on Operational Research (1960), p. 237.

53 Ventura, E., *Étude du roulage dans une mine par les méthodes de simulation*, Proceedings of the Second International Conference on Operational Research (1960), p. 633.

54 Clapham, J. C. R., 'A Monte Carlo Problem in Underground Communications', *Operational Research Quarterly*, March 1958, p. 36.

55 Lathrop, J. B., *The Application of Operational Research Methods to Transport*, Proceedings of the Second International Conference on Operational Research (1960), p. 647.

56 Edwards, J. A., 'Simulating traffic flow problems on a Computer', *Data Processing*, July-September 1962, p. 192.

57 Adams, R. H., and Jenkins, J. L., 'Simulation of Air Operations with the Air-Battle Model', *Operations Research*, September–October 1960, p. 600.

58 Davies, O. L. (ed.), *The Design and Analysis of Industrial Experiments* (Oliver & Boyd 1956).

59 Conway, R. W., Johnson, B. M., and Maxwell, W. L., 'Some Problems of Digital Systems Simulation', *Management Science*, October 1959, p. 92.

60 Harling, J., 'Simulation Techniques in Operational Research', *Operational Research Quarterly*, March 1958, p. 9.

61 Youle, P. V., Tocher, H. D., Jessop, W. N., and Musk, F. J., 'Simulation Studies of Industrial Operations', *Journal of the Royal Statistical Society*, Series A, 1959 (Part 4), p. 484.

62 Tocher, K. D., 'The Role of Models in Operational Research', *Journal of the Royal Statistical Society*, Series A, 1961 (Part II), p. 121.

63 Malcolm, D. G., 'Bibliography on the Use of Simulation in Management Analysis', *Operations Research*, March–April 1961, p. 169.

64 Bacon, Francis (1561–1626), Essay *Of Simulation and Dissimulation*.

65 Tocher, K. D., *The Art of Simulation* (E.U.P., 1963), p. 73.

66 Forrester, J., *Industrial Dynamics* (Wiley, 1961).

8

Computers and Common Sense

The tools of working out salvation
By mere mechanic operation.

SAMUEL BUTLER, *Hudibras*

INTRODUCTION

How does a manager set about using an electronic computer?
Suppose he is a man with no great knowledge of mathematics,
working for a company which has neither a computer nor the
money to buy one: must he then banish the idea from his
mind? So often he does, yet he need not. Let us see how he
should go about it, taking as an example the aircraft maintenance project described in Chapter 2.

First he selects a computer service bureau. Then he asks
whether they have a standard routine which will do the sort
of work he wants. If they have, he sets out the problem in a
standard form and selects the way in which he wants the
answer printed. Then he gets his answer back; then he pays
the bill.

We shall first look at this procedure in more detail; after that
we shall see what happens when a standard routine is not
available, and then we shall consider some of the wider
implications.

FINDING A SERVICE BUREAU

How do you start? The answer may be right under your nose.
So many companies have in their ranks a bright young man
who has more spare time than the harassed manager, and whose
natural curiosity and enthusiasm have led him into the
professional circles where computers are talked about. Catch
him before frustration drives him elsewhere, enlist his aid,

and watch him flower. (If you cannot find such a man, perhaps you should transfer your own attention from computer applications to the wider issues of management succession in your firm.)

The nearest university or technical college would be the next source of information. Some of them have computers of their own, which they may run either independently or in collaboration with the manufacturers. You may, if you are lucky, get your work done for nothing. This is most likely to occur if you are willing to release the information for teaching or demonstration purposes afterwards. More probably, you will have to pay for the use of the machine at the same rates as the manufacturer himself would charge. What is quite certain is that any academic institution will do its utmost to give you helpful and unbiased advice.

Your search will most probably end in one of the service bureaux run by a manufacturer. If it does, you should realize at the outset that the manufacturer's main purpose is to sell or lease the machines he makes, and the service bureau is only a means to this end. However, this attitude is already changing; the idea of running a few very big computers as a public service has already taken root in the United States and will soon spread to Europe.

In the meantime, England has more computing service facilities, relative to its needs, than any other country, including the United States. One British manufacturer is even experimenting with a 'launderette' service where customers themselves are allowed to operate the machines. Most of the bureaux are in London, but many have been established in provincial cities; lists of them are published from time to time in the computer journals.

The final selection of a bureau must inevitably depend on guesswork, friendly advice and the manager's native shrewdness. A big manufacturer may have a wider range of standard routines and plenty of expert help available (at an appropriate fee). A smaller one may, on the other hand, be able to offer more personal attention. The bureau chosen for the example in this chapter is not necessarily better or worse than the others.

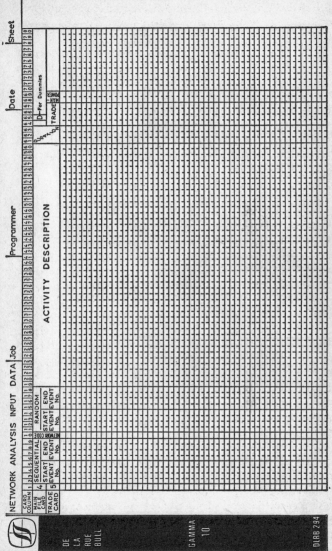

Fig. 8.1 Standard input form for network analysis

CARD COLUMN	MAIN FILE CARD 4 SEQUENTIAL 5 RANDOM				NETWORK CODE	ACTIVITY DESCRIPTION	TRADE CARD 5 MAN POWER	D-For Dummies
	START EVENT No.	END EVENT No.	START EVENT No.	END EVENT No.			TRADE / MAN POWER	
4	1	2				PREPARE FOR INSPECTION	1	
4	2	3				INSPECT AIRFRAME	10	
4	2	4				CLEAN & REMOVE WHEELS	4	
4	4	15				UNPANEL ENGINES	3	
4	3	30				RECTIFY AIRFRAME	28	
4	4	5				INSPECT MAIN WHEELS	17	
4	5	6				RECTIFY MAIN WHEELS	16	
4	5	7				RECTIFY MAIN WHEELS	9	
4	7	16				RECTIFY NOSE WHEEL	8	
4	10	11				TEST & RECTIFY RADIO	6	
4	10	12				RECHARGE EMERGENCY SYSTEM	3	
4	10	13				RECTIFY RETRACTION	13	
4	11	30				DUMMY	D	
4	12	14				LUBRICATE	13	
4	13	14				CHECK INSTRUMENTS	14	
4	14	30				CHECK LUBRICATION	24	
4	15	16				RECTIFY INSTRUMENTS	11	
4	16	17				CLEAN STARBOARD ENGINE	21	
4	17	18				INSPECT PORT ENGINE	D	
4	18	19				DUMMY	30	
4	20	21				RECTIFY PORT ENGINE	20	
4	20	22				DUMMY	D	
4	21	23				INSPECT STARBOARD ENGINE	D	
4	22	23				INSPECT FIRE EXTINGUISHERS	12	
4	23	30				RECTIFY STARBOARD ENGINE	30	
4	30	31				GENERAL CHECK	1	

Fig. 8.2 Completed input form

THE PROBLEM

The manager must know what his problem is, and must have reduced it to a calculation or a series of calculations. It is unreasonable to expect a computing service to analyse a practical situation in a business. In the example chosen, the arrow diagram for overhauling the aircraft must have already been drawn up by skilled men, and the durations estimated. It is only necessary to lay it out in the standard input form shown in Figure 8.1.

INPUT FORM

This form is arranged in columns, indicated by the short vertical strokes along each row. The two top rows ('Card Column') identify each column, the total number being 80 (to correspond with the standard punched card).

The method of entering the data is shown in Figure 8.2 and is obvious apart from one or two points. The letter 'I' has to be distinguishable from the figure '1' and zero is written as 'Ø', so as not to be confused with the letter 'O'. The entry '4' in the first column is a coding required by the computer, as are the *D*'s in column 65 wherever the row describes a dummy activity.

The manager will also be asked to supply some further information, such as the time units in which the data are expressed (in this case, hours), the amount of float which defines a sub-critical path (we have chosen 10 hours), and the way in which the output should be presented. As far as he is concerned, the work of preparing the input is now complete. The data are fed to the computer in a suitable form, and the output appears as shown in Figure 8.3. Compare it with Table 2.1: apart from minor differences in layout, they are identical.

The bill for this particular job was

Punching, verifying and sorting cards:	8s. 0d.
Computer time (Gamma 10 machine, 5 mins):	£1 5s. 0d.
Total:	£1 13s. 0d.

The Gamma 10 is a computer designed primarily for commercial data processing; but it can also effectively handle technical and Management Science applications including Scientific Inventory Management, Statistical Forecasting, Linear Programming, Simulation, Production Control and Network Analysis.
This Network Analysis Programme is a practical system for planning and controlling large projects involving construction, manufacture, research and development, etc.
It uses the standard Critical Path Scheduling technique but with a number of refinements and extensions.
It also exploits special features of the machine so as to produce a range of sophisticated analyses, including random numbering of events; calendar date output with allowance for holidays and weekends; scheduled start dates for individual activities, items and machines; detailed work schedules for foremen; manpower aggregation and levelling; and cost forecasting and control.

DE LA RUE BULL
Machines Limited
114 Southampton Row, London, W.C.I.
Area Offices in Birmingham, Bristol, Dublin, Glasgow and Manchester.

DATE: 040565   DE LA RUE BULL   NETWORK ANALYSIS PROGRAMME   GAMMA 10   PAGE 1

PROJECT: SCHEDULE FOR AIRCRFT OVERHAUL
FLOAT LIMIT: 10
C/P DURATION: 66
NUMBER OF EVENTS: 21

DIVISION: PLANNING
TIME UNIT: HOURS
NUMBER OF ACTIVITIES: 29

REPORT: ALL ACTIVITIES

CRITICAL	NEAR CRITICAL	START EVENT	END EVENT	NETWORK CODE	ACTIVITY	TRACE	MAN-POWER	DURATION	START EARLIEST	START LATEST	END EARLIEST	END LATEST	TOTAL FLOAT
•		1	2		PREPARE FOR INSPECTION			1				4	
•		15	15		UNPANEL ENGINES			5	4	4	4	9	10
•		16	16		CLEAN PORT ENGINE			24	5	5	5	29	0
•		17	30		INSPECT PORT ENGINE			36	29	29	29	65	10
					RECTIFY PORT ENGINE				65	65	65	65	21
•		30	31		GENERAL CHECK			1	65	65	66	66	
		15	20		CLEAN STARBOARD ENGINE			1	4	15	5	35	26
		25	23		INSPECT STARBOARD ENGINE			20	25	35	25	55	10
		23	12		RECTIFY STARBOARD ENGINE			30	25	22	52	23	21
		12			UNPANEL FOR LUB. ETC.								
		12	14		CHECK INSTRUMENTS			18	20	23	20	41	21
		14	30		RECTIFY INSTRUMENTS			24	1	27	41	37	26
		23	30		INSPECT AIRFRAME			28	39	37	39	65	26
		32	4		RECTIFY AIRFRAME			24	1	41	35	45	40
					CLEAN, REMOVE WHEELS								
		4	5		INSPECT MAIN WHEELS			7	5	45	12	52	40
		5	100		RECTIFY MAIN WHEELS			9	12	52	21	61	40
		7	300		TEST RETRACTION			3	22	62	22	65	40
		10	7		INSPECT RETRACTION			6	1	47	21	53	42
					INSPECT NOSE WHEEL								
		10	11		RECTIFY NOSE WHEEL			8	11	53	19	61	42
		2	22		RECHARGE EMERGENCY SYSTEM			2	22	52	27	54	47
		22	13		INSPECT FIRE EXTINGUISHERS			1	7	54	18	65	47
		12			RECTIFY FIRE EXTINGUISHERS			3	2	61	5	64	59
					LUBRICATE								
		13	30		CHECK LUBRICATION			1	5	64	6	65	59

Fig. 8.3 Network analysis programme: schedule for aircraft overhaul

In practice, a minimum charge is applied. In this bureau it would have been £10, but for this sum one could obtain a similar analysis of a network of 200 jobs.

Let us now look at some of the items in this procedure in more detail, beginning with the computing routine itself.

STANDARD ROUTINES

Standard computing routines are always available for widely-used techniques such as network analysis or linear programming, and the range over which they extend is constantly widening. They are often referred to as 'library programs' or under the general term 'software'. In the early days of commercial computers, the makers put far too much emphasis on the machine itself – the hardware – and too little on the software, but this mistake is rapidly being corrected.

Programs in general will be discussed at greater length later: for the moment it is enough to understand that they turn the general-purpose computer into a machine which can carry out a specific calculation – in our example, finding a critical path. The calculation is always carried out within certain limits imposed either by the machine itself or the nature of the computing routine: they are set out in a Program Specification.

The specification sets out in detail what the program will do and what are its limitations. For example, a network analysis routine may only be able to accept networks of up to a certain size, as defined by the number of events or activities.

Some of the characteristics of the program we used may be seen by studying Figure 8.1. We could have dispensed with the ij rule in numbering our original network, because this program can accept and analyse a randomly-numbered network: we have only to enter the event numbers into columns 11 to 18 instead of columns 2 to 9. Had we done so, the cost of computation would have been greater, because the machine would have re-numbered the network before analysing it.

The specification also tells us that we can suppress the printing of dummy activities in the output by entering the letter D in column 65, as we did on the input form. Other

entries in columns 64 to 69 would enable us to enter the manpower requirements in various trade categories as input, and
obtain aggregated figures for the manpower requirements at
each stage of the project.

The specification sets out the limitations of the size of
numbers: as is obvious from Figure 8.1, the largest permissible number for an event is 9999. The duration of an activity
is limited to three digits, and the specification tells us the
range of time units in which the duration can be expressed.

In some cases, the specification may contain a formula for
calculating roughly how long the computer will take to complete the calculation. A preliminary estimate of the cost could
then be made.

OUTPUT FACILITIES

Modern computer programs may offer a choice of various
styles and layouts for the output which is usually called the
'print-out'. At one time, the output consisted of strings of
figures and abbreviations which were difficult to decipher;
then routines for tabulating the data were developed; now the
computer can be made to present documents which are suitable for direct use by managers.

Figure 8.4 gives a good illustration of the versatility of
computer routines and the wide range of output layouts, because it was produced by the same network analysis program
which dealt with our aircraft overhaul. The complete network
for launching a new product had been fed into the computer,
with each individual activity coded to show the department
('trade') responsible for doing it. After analysing the network,
the machine sorted the output into nine separate groups
corresponding to the nine departments concerned and printed
each group on a separate sheet. Figure 8.4 is the sheet corresponding to the Marketing Department (trade code M). A
starting date was fed in with the input, and the event times
were translated into calendar dates by one of the optional
facilities of the routine. Only the earliest event times are
printed out, and they are simply described as 'programmed

DIVISION: RUN :
PROJECT: DREAMSWEET PRODUCT LAUNCH

DEPARTMENT: MARKETING MANAGER
DATE: 13 APR 65
PAGE: 8

TRADE	START EVENT	END EVENT	DESCRIPTION	NP	DUR	PROGRAMMED START	ACTUAL START	PROGRAMMED FINISH	ACTUAL FINISH	REMARKS
00	3	4	PREPARE NEW PRODUCT MEMO NPM		6	18 MAY 65		21 MAY 65		
00	4	10	SEND NPM TO MARKET RESEARCH			21 MAY 65		21 MAY 65		
00	4	7	SEND NPM TO PRODUCTION			21 MAY 65		21 MAY 65		
00	4	5	SEND NPM TO RESEARCH			21 MAY 65		21 MAY 65		
00	4	11	SEND NPM TO ADVERTISING AGENCY			21 MAY 65		21 MAY 65		
00	4	6	SEND NPM TO BUYER			21 MAY 65		21 MAY 65		
00	17	21	FORECAST SALES		10	21 JUN 65		25 JUN 65		
00	21	30	BEGIN TO PREPARE NEW PRODUCT AUTHORITY NPA		10	28 JUN 65		2 JLY 65		
00	21	22	SEND SALES FORECAST TO PRODUCTION			25 JUN 65		25 JUN 65		
00	30	31	COMPLETE NPA		4	21 JLY 65		22 JLY 65		
00	31	43	SEND NPA TO MARKET RESEARCH			22 JLY 65		22 JLY 65		
00	31	45	PREPARE SALES CONFERENCE		60	23 JLY 65		2 SEP 65		
00	31	34	SEND NPA TO ADVERTISING AGENCY			22 JLY 65		22 JLY 65		
00	31	33	SEND NPA TO PRODUCTION			22 JLY 65		22 JLY 65		
00	31	32	SEND NPA TO BUYER			22 JLY 65		22 JLY 65		
00	45	46	RUN SALES CONFERENCE		4	4 OCT 65		9 OCT 65		

Fig. 8.4 Departmental schedule prepared by computer

start' and 'programmed finish'; the critical path and floats are described in a master print-out elsewhere but are suppressed in this part of the output, presumably on the grounds that the Marketing Department might adopt a dangerous '*laissez-faire*' attitude if it knew that some activities had large floats.

The output has also been made to include 'actual start', 'actual finish' and 'remarks', so that it can be filled in directly, returned as a progress report by the Marketing Manager, and used to prepare an amended input for re-scheduling the product launch if the given dates have not been met. (The cost of the complete analysis was about £5.)

PREPARING THE INPUT

How are the data in Figure 8.2 put into the computer? Most modern computers take in both the program and the figures as standard 80-column punched cards. Punch operators put the cards into a punching machine with a keyboard, by means of which they transcribe each figure (or letter) into a hole (or two holes), the position of which corresponds to the value of the corresponding digit.

Figure 8.5 shows the card for the first activity in the aircraft overhaul. Each column has ten positions, numbered from 0 to 9. The identification number of every second column is also printed in fine type between 0 and 1 and again between 8 and 9. This card has been prepared in a machine which also types the character corresponding to the punch-hole, so it is easy to see that the start event number '1' is represented by a hole in row 1 of column 5. Letters are represented by two holes in the same column.

Exercise 8.1

The letter 'R' in the word 'FOR' is represented by two holes. Where are they?

Great care is taken to ensure that cards are punched accurately. Two entirely separate operators prepare packs of cards corresponding to the same set of data, and these duplicated

Fig. 8.5 Punched card for first activity

packs are then compared by a machine called a 'verifier'. If the cards in any identical pair fail to agree, the verifier indicates the error. Thus the only possibility of error in the input is for two operators to make exactly the same mistake, which is unlikely. Computers themselves also contain elaborate checking devices.

When the cards are fed into the machine, they pass through a card-reader which detects the holes and their positions with the aid of photo-electric cells. These cells generate electrical impulses corresponding to the appropriate numbers, which are fed into the computer.

The labour needed to punch tapes or cards has always presented a problem to the users of electronic computers. The 'mark-sensed' card is one of the means used to reduce the effort of preparing data; numbers are marked on a card in the appropriate columns with a pencil containing a magnetic 'lead'. A set of magnetic sensing devices then detects the location of each mark and converts it into electrical pulses.

The ideal input machine would be one which could read input directly from printed or even written documents, and some progress has been made in developing one. The Electronic Reading Automaton (E.R.A.) produced by Solartron uses photoelectric cells to detect the pattern of light and dark squares generated by superimposing a scanning grid on to printed numbers. Figure 8.6 shows how the light and dark squares are generated, and how they may be represented by digits, with '1' representing a shaded square and '0' an unshaded one. The machine has the ability to compare the sets of digits with standard patterns stored in it, and thus translate the patterns back into the original numbers. One such machine is in service with Montague Burton Ltd, 'reading', at a speed of 400 digits per second, the tally rolls from cash registers and producing punched cards from them. More modern machines such as the R.C.A. 'Videoscan' use scanning methods similar to those of television and can read up to 1,500 characters a second.

An alternative to optical scanning is to use characters printed in magnetic ink. The MICR system (Magnetic Ink Character Recognition) is mainly used by banks, and the specially designed characters are now becoming a familiar feature of our

Fig. 8.6 Digital representation of figures

cheque-books. The digits are distorted into shapes which, when printed in magnetic ink, can be readily distinguished by magnetic reading heads while still recognizable by the human eye.

Difficulties in the field of mechanical perception are many – size and alignment of characters, similarities such as 5 and S or I and 1, and defective printing all constitute major problems – but a considerable research effort is being applied to them and it seems only a matter of time before computers will be taking their information direct from the printed page.

ORGANIZATION OF A COMPUTER

The detailed mechanisms which enable a computer to do its work so quickly and accurately are of little interest to the manager. They are often over-emphasized, so that the unfortunate layman is left with a bewildering jumble of impressions about binary arithmetic, logical switching circuits, transistors and the like, which are not really relevant.

It is, however, useful to know the broad areas into which an electronic computer is divided, if only to dispel some of the myths which have accumulated around these machines. They

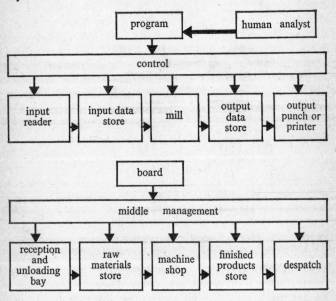

Fig. 8.7 Organizations of electronic computer and engineering factory

are illustrated in Fig. 8.7, which also shows a factory organization for comparison.

The complex switching circuits which perform arithmetical and logical operations are the very heart of an electronic computer. It is they that do the 'processing' of the data which are fed to them, and in this sense they are similar to the machine shop of an engineering works or the weaving shed of a textile factory. The resemblance led Charles Babbage to coin the word 'mill' for this part of any calculating engine.

The rest of a computer is built around the mill in much the same way as a conventional factory. The input is taken in as already described, stored as 'raw material' until needed, then fed to the mill and processed; the 'finished' products – output data – are stored until needed and then sent to an output mechanism. All this needs a control – the middle 'management' of the computer – which is held in the internal circuits of the machine.

This built-in control carries out the routine tasks necessary to the efficient internal working of the machine. There is, however, a form of control at a still higher level, corresponding to the policy-making board of a manufacturing company. This is the program of instructions which dictates to the machine exactly what series of calculations it must perform. The ability to accept and act on a program is one of the characteristics which raise an electronic computer far above the level of conventional calculating machines; the other is its speed.

THE PROGRAM

When we use an ordinary desk calculator, we feed in one number to be stored, and then press either the '+' key or the '−' key. By doing so, we prepare or 'program' the machine to add or to subtract the next number to be fed in. The equivalent in an electronic computer is some internal switching arrangement which will program the machine to add. It will be constructed in such a way that a particular set of electrical impulses will operate it, and the set of impulses will correspond to the input of a certain code symbol. Thus, the letter A could mean 'add', the letter S, 'subtract' and the letter M, 'multiply.' The coded instruction, like the numbers themselves, will be fed in by a suitably punched card.

If we have a string of numbers to add on a desk-calculator, we have to keep on pushing the '+' key as each new number is fed in. The electronic computer, on the other hand, can accept and apply a whole sequence of instructions, such as

Read in the first number
Read in the second number
Add the two together to give a sub-total
Read in the third number
Subtract it from the sub-total
Print out the answer

This sequence, when written in the appropriate program code, might be expressed as:

R 1
R 2
A 1 & 2
R 3
S 3
P

This is a very simple form of computer programming, analogous to assembling a few parts in an engineering shop. The programmer has a much greater job of internal management to specify – getting data into and out of the machine, moving blocks of it around from one store to the other, even making such decisions as when to scrap information (which is what we do when we 'round off' a number). How does his work compare with that of managing a business?

In a real factory, the manager can rely to some extent on the training his men have already received. For instance instead of specifying the following operations in detail:

Pick up nut with left hand
Pick up bolt with right hand
Bring nut and bolt together
Align nut and bolt
Push nut on to end of bolt
Turn nut
Repeat turn until nut is tight
Release nut from left hand
Release bolt from right hand,

he can simply issue the overall instruction 'Assemble nut to bolt'. The detailed instructions are already stored as a sub-routine in the man's brain because they are needed so often. If the man were completely unskilled, the manager could still make life easier for himself by having a prepared card available with 'Assemble nut to bolt' as the heading and the program of instructions set out underneath. The man could then teach himself the job.

The computer programmer can organize his own work in a similar way. He can draw up a series of instructions such as

Put $y = 1$
Divide a by y
Add the quotient to y
Halve the sum and use it as a new value of y
Repeat all but the first instruction until further changes in y cannot be detected
Replace a by y

and, after translating them into machine language, punch them on to a set of cards entitled 'Replace a by its square root'.

Exercise 8.2

Putting $a = 100$, check that this series of instructions will replace it by its square root. Do not work to more than four decimal places.

Other sub-routines may deal with cube and higher roots, powers of numbers, logarithms and trigonometrical functions. They are usually written by the manufacturers' programming staff and assembled into a 'library' on punched cards. In this way, the standard computing routines already mentioned are built up.

Programming is not quite so simple as this brief description makes it sound. For one thing, every eventuality must be foreseen: suppose that a network contains a loop which has remained undetected because the events were numbered randomly. When the machine attempts to re-number the network sequentially, it will meet an impossible situation and may stop. On the other hand, it may go on trying over and over again. A good program will stop the machine; a better program may signal the nature of the fault, by printing out 'LOOP', an even better one may print out not only the type of fault, but its location also. The skill, forethought and ingenuity of the programmer play a great part in ensuring the efficiency and versatility of programs.

Commercial operations may also be reduced to standard routines: examples are converting decimals of a pound sterling to shillings and pence, or working out tax deductions for compiling payrolls.

Many computer manufacturers have formed users' associations, whose members contribute new standard routines to the library as well as exchanging more specialized programs amongst themselves.

To complete the picture, one must include the standard routines which are permanently built into a computer to deal with essential matters such as starting-up and testing. Unlike programs received through the input, they cannot be erased.

Finally there are the 'compiler' routines which make programming easier. When they are fed into the machine, they set it up so that it can accept instructions in a different 'language' from its normal code. Taking an earlier example, the series of instructions R1, R2, A1 & 2, R3, S3, P could be generated by a suitable compiler routine from the input $t = a + b - c$.

Compilers also help to make electronic computers interchangeable. The machines made by one manufacturer will have their own particular programming code and those of a second manufacturer will have a different one. If each manufacturer prepares a compiler routine which will translate instructions in some universal 'language' into a program in his own code, then programs written in the universal language can be run on any machine. Such universal languages already exist: they include FORTRAN (Formula Translator), COBOL (Common Business-Oriented Language) and ALGOL (Algebra-Oriented Language).

At one time it was hoped that compilers would become so simple that any layman could learn to program a machine in a few hours. To some extent this has been achieved, and many scientists can prepare simple programs to aid them in their calculations. In general, though, some skilled help will always be needed when a new computing routine is to be created. The problem is especially difficult for managers, since computers can only deal with Q-factors.

In general, applying an electronic computer to management problems takes place in two stages, systems analysis and machine coding. The second of these has already been described: the programmer knows at the outset what the calculation is, and has only to translate it into machine language. The other is the far more difficult job of reducing a business problem to a prescribed calculation: this is called Systems Analysis. Sometimes it is straightforward: in putting a payroll calculation on to a computer, the work is first broken down into sections such as basic rates, overtime, piecework rates, incentive bonus, tax deductions and so on. A sub-routine is written for each section and the complete program is then built up. A cynic has observed that a payroll calculation is always a good starting point for a new computer, because so many people can be relied on to check the output in great detail.

The work of a Systems Analyst will be more difficult when he comes to deal with business procedures which are not quite so clear-cut; for example, what is the set of rules which a despatcher uses in making up loads for vehicles and deciding their routes? Even the man himself does not know how he reaches his decisions, and methods for obtaining optimum solutions are not yet known. Empirical rules, trial-and-error and statistically designed experiments may all have to be called to the analyst's aid. Whatever the problem, he is almost certain to attack it by drawing up a logical flowsheet.

FLOWSHEETS

We have already met logical flowsheets in Chapter 7, so the example given in Figure 8.8 should look familiar. It represents a simple stock-checking routine; the sausage-shaped 'decision boxes' mark all those points in the system where the next part of the procedure depends upon a test of some numerical value. Box 5 tests whether the stock is at or below the Re-Ordering

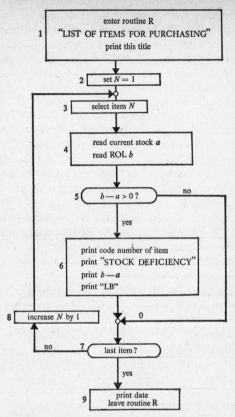

Fig. 8.8 Flowsheet for stock-checking routine

Level. If it is, the item goes into the list to be considered for purchasing (Box 6). If the stock is above the ROL, the item is passed over.

The loop is linked up between Box 7 and Box 3 with the aid of the counter N, and enables the same simple routine to examine a large number of items. The capacity to obey looped routines is one of the most powerful weapons in the programmer's hands, and flowsheets will often contain loops within loops. One must always make provision for getting out of loops as well as entering them; this is done by having a decision box – Box 7 in this example – which tests whether the routine should leave the loop or not. A counter is usually the subject of the test: here it is N. If we know the total number of stock items to be checked – call it M – then the test in Box 7 could be simply

$$N = M?$$

The need for Box 7 illustrates one of the weaknesses of computers which most programmers learn painfully through their initial mistakes. You cannot rely on the common sense of an electronic computer, for it has none. In this respect it is a moron, and must be told how to recognize the last item, and to stop when it is reached. Otherwise, it will go on trying to read non-existent data until something breaks down. Neither is it enough to instruct the machine to divide x by y: one must first test that y is not zero.

Exercise 8.3

Use the following list to work through the flowsheet of Figure 8.8 and produce an exception list.

Item No.	Current Stock, lb.	ROL, lb.
N	a	b
1	316	200
2	150	100
3	75	75
4	369	120
5	12	50
6	0	100

Exercise 8.4

Insert an extra test in Figure 8.8 so that Item No. 3 and others like it will be shown as being just on the Re-Ordering Level.

Exercise 8.5

The flowsheet (Figure 8.9) for finding a square root by the method described earlier is arranged to print out the answer as soon as successive estimates differ by less than 0.01. There is an error in the testing method. Can you detect and correct it? If not, try working through a specimen calculation for $a = 0.5$.

Fig. 8.9

COST OF PROGRAMMING

It must now be obvious that the operation known loosely as 'putting a job on to a computer' is neither easy nor cheap. The demand for computer programmers and systems analysts has grown at a faster rate than the supply, and the facilities for training such men are still inadequate. In consequence, their salaries are high. Detailed analysis of management systems always take longer than one expects, and computer programs do not always work properly the first time. They have to be checked and revised, in the procedure known as 'de-bugging'. The whole process may well consume several man-years of highly skilled work.

The initial cost of programming is therefore high: it can easily run into hundreds or thousands of pounds, even for a relatively simple job. Nevertheless, the situation is already much better than it was a few years ago, and is constantly improving. The advent of compiler routines has already been mentioned: simultaneously, some manufacturers have been developing 'building bricks'. In these, certain complex calculations (such as forecasting procedures) which constantly recur in business problems, are available in a form which can be readily 'slotted in' to bigger programs.

DECISION BOXES

The tests in the decision boxes are no more than traffic signals based on simple logical rules, but some of the consequences of this simple mechanism are far-reaching. It is not difficult to imagine an extension to the flowsheet in Figure 8.8 which would refer to a master file when stock was too low and then set in motion a sub-routine for producing a purchase order, even comparing suppliers' prices and selecting the lower if required to do so. Such procedures do in fact exist. This 'decision-making' power of a computer has given rise to some gross misconceptions. Imagine a personnel officer specifying that, for a particular job, a man should have a degree, an intelligence quotient greater than 120 and be not less than 5′ 8″ tall. A flow sheet can easily be drawn up for selecting the cards corresponding to suitable people from a file pack: this was done, even before computers were available, by the conventional punched card machinery of WOCCI, the War Office Central Card Index. How easy it is to misrepresent this as a machine making a decision about a human being's suitability for a job! This is misplaced anthropomorphism.

We have been warned, by Lorentz and others, not to attribute human emotions and qualities to animals whose behaviour resembles our own. The same warning needs to be repeated about electronic computers. Because electrical engineers have adopted certain jargon terms, such as 'memory' for a store of data; because the machine can be made to imitate learning by suitable programs; because irresponsible or ill-informed writers have labelled them 'electronic brains'; because they can be made to select alternative courses of action; because the finer details of their construction are beyond the comprehension of a layman, these machines have been credited with human or even superhuman attributes and elevated to the status of the businessman's bogy-man.

The computer will make all managers redundant. . . .
The computer will be the next chess champion. . . .
The computer will start the next nuclear war. . . .
The computer says. . . .

The computer says no more than it has been told to say. The most important difference between the two diagrams in Figure 8.7 is the heavy black arrow showing that the management of the machine is imposed on it by an outside agency and not generated spontaneously from within.

The real danger lies in ascribing to the output of computers a sanctity which it does not possess. The program under which it operates may have been drawn up by a man who knows all about the machine but nothing about the business. He may have written a program to calculate economic lot sizes and inserted his own value of that most important figure, the required return on capital. Or he may have devised a method for allocating routes to delivery vehicles which has never been tested in practice. It has truly been said of electronic computers that, whatever else they do, they will faithfully reproduce in their output all the errors of the input, and this applies as much to the logical structure of the program as it does to the numerical value of the data. And a computer cannot fire the first ICBM of a nuclear war unless some human fool wires it up to do so.

When it comes to chess, the situation is less clearly defined. Unless the programmer has a deep insight into the game he is unlikely to write a good set of instructions for winning. Never-theless, he has at his command the power to evaluate hundreds or thousands of alternative moves in great detail and at high speed, as long as the evaluation follows rigidly prescribed rules. It is here that we see the computer at its most efficient, as an amplifier of the human brain. The combination of human insight and the mindless calculating ability of electronic machinery might well produce a new chess champion half flesh and blood, half wires and transistors, but the computer will never, never do it alone.

8

Solutions to Exercises

Exercise 8.1

In positions 6 and 8 of column 29.

Exercise 8.2

a	y	$\dfrac{a}{y}$	$\dfrac{a}{y} + y$
100	1·0000	100·0000	101·0000
	50·5000	1·9802	52·4802
	26·2401	3·8110	30·0511
	15·0256	6·6553	21·6809
	10·8404	9·2248	20·0652
	10·0326	9·9675	20·0001
	10·0000		

Exercise 8.3

LIST OF ITEMS FOR PURCHASING.
5 STOCK DEFICIENCY 38 LB.
6 STOCK DEFICIENCY 100 LB.
12 NOVEMBER 1965

Exercise 8.4

Exercise 8.5

$$a = 0 \cdot 5$$
$$y = 1$$
$$p = a/y = 0 \cdot 5$$
$$q = y + p = 1 \cdot 5$$
$$r = q/2 = 0 \cdot 75$$
$$s = r - y = -0 \cdot 25$$

Is $s < 0 \cdot 01$? Yes, because s is preceded by a negative sign, and the calculation stops. We need to test the *absolute* value of s; one way of doing so is

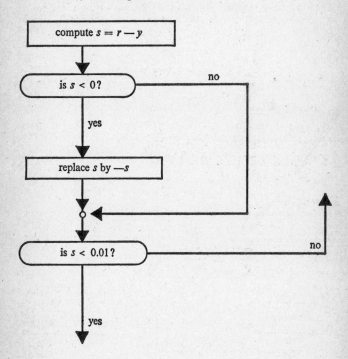

NOTES AND REFERENCES

67 Battersby, A., *Chemistry and Industry*, 15 November 1957, p. 1488.
68 Roach Pierson, D., *Data and Control*, November 1963, p. 27.
69 Kemeny, J. G., Schlaifer, Snell, and Thomson, *Finite Mathematics with Business Applications* (Prentice-Hall, 1962), p. 40.
70 Bowden, B. V., *Faster than Thought* (Pitman, 1963), chaps 1–5.
71 De Paris, J., *Data Processing for Management*, September 1963, p. 22.
72 Elmaghraby, S. E., *Management Science* (1964), p. 494.

The September 1966 issue of *Scientific American* is entirely devoted to 'Information'; it contains much up-to-date news about computers.

9
Curves and Capital

I'm very well acquainted too with matters mathematical,
I understand equations, both the simple and quadratical.

W. S. GILBERT, *The Pirates of Penzance*

WE have seen how much can be accomplished with no more
than simple linear functions, but inevitably we shall reach a
stage where linear functions cannot adequately represent the
true relationships between factors in the real world. The
average temperature is not a linear function of the time of
year, and neither are the sales of goods which depend on it,
be they winter overcoats or beer; the amount of a chemical
produced in a reaction may increase at a slower rate as the
reaction proceeds; the rate of growth of demand for electricity
follows a steepening curve, and so on.

Because linear relationships are so easy to handle mathematically, several methods of turning non-linear functions into
linear ones are used in practice. One is to break up a curved
line into a number of short straight ones: such a method has
been described by Garvin[73] for dealing with the relationship
between the amount of TEL (tetra-ethyl lead) added to motor
spirit and the octane number which measures the anti-knock
properties of the blend. The graph of the true curve is shown
in Figure 9.1, the linear approximation in Figure 9.2. The
TEL is divided into five imaginary types, with restrictions imposed so that all of 'Type 1' must be used before any 'Type 2'
is added, and so on.

Another method is to 'transform' the data. Figure 9.3, shows
the cost of binding, per book, plotted against the size of the
order. Figure 9.4 shows the same relationship transformed into
a straight line by plotting the total cost of the order instead of
the cost per book.

This is our old acquaintance from Chapter 3,

$$y = mx + c \qquad (9.1)$$

Fig. 9.1 True relationship between TEL and octane number

We can interpret this equation by saying that for any order there is a fixed cost c which does not depend on the size of the order: in Figure 9.4 it is £25. There is also a cost m, the variable cost per book, which *is* directly proportional to the size of the order.

The *total* cost per book (call it b) is m plus some share of the fixed cost c which must also be borne by the book. Expressed mathematically:

$$b = y/x = m + c/x \qquad (9.2)$$

Fig. 9.2 Linear approximation to TEL/octane number graph

Fig. 9.3 Cost of binding books, per book

This is the equation of the curve in Figure 9.3, which is a hyperbola. Considering the process in reverse, we may say that by multiplying equation (9.2) by x throughout, we have transformed it into the linear equation (9.1).

Fig. 9.4 Cost of binding books, total for order

Problems in which a fixed charge has to be spread over a number of items are frequently encountered by managers. The number bought or made may be varied at the discretion of a manager: thus the cost of setting up a production line may be allocated over the number of items subsequently made by it, or the cost of taxing and insuring a motor vehicle may be included in a mileage charge. (There is a story about an accountant with a Rolls-Royce who said, 'It is ruinously expensive to run, but I just *have* to go to work in it every day: it's the only way I can keep the cost down to less than half-a-crown a mile.') Both these examples were encountered as linear functions in Chapter 3, and Pascal's Pressings (Exercise 3.2) provide a useful starting point. The equation for the total cost y (in shillings) of a batch of spacing pieces was found to be

$$y = 0 \cdot 25x + 600 \qquad (9.3)$$

in which x is the number of pieces ordered. The total cost per piece, b, is found by dividing both sides of the equation by x:

$$b = \frac{y}{x} = 0 \cdot 25 + \frac{600}{x} \qquad (9.4)$$

Compare this equation with (9.2). Its graph, in Figure 9.5, gives a picture of the familiar 'economy of scale' which results from spreading the fixed costs over a large number of items.

Exercise 9.1

The cost of tax, insurance and hire purchase instalments for a motor-lorry in a single year is £1,200; petrol, oil and maintenance cost 1s. 6d. a mile and we assume there are no other charges. Draw a graph showing the total cost per mile for yearly mileages in the range 6,000 to 24,000, and write down its equation, using shillings as the unit.

CONFLICTING GOALS

Economies of scale – low costs through high output – are generally recognized as desirable aims for any business, but the other side of the picture is often neglected. There may be

Fig. 9.5 Economy of scale

some costs which *increase* as the scale of manufacture in-creases, notably those connected with the financing of the business.

Suppose that Pascal's Pressings are in a situation differing only slightly from the one already described: we are no longer concerned with the cost of the initial tools, but rather with the preparations for manufacture of repeated batches. There are again certain fixed jobs (and therefore costs) which do not depend on the number to be made: issuing the authority to manufacture, drawing the tools from stores, fitting them to the machine and adjusting it, and so on; the sum of all these fixed costs is the setting-up cost, which amounts to £5 (100 shillings). Material and labour costs, together with services such as electricity and lubrication, come to 1s. for each part.

Then the cost per unit, in shillings, is given by equation (9.5), where x is the number in the batch.

$$c = 1 + \frac{100}{x} \qquad (9.5)$$

The Production Manager has to decide how many to make in this batch, and has tentatively picked a figure of 10,000 (equal to the current yearly demand for these pieces). Equation 9.5 gives the cost per piece as 1·01 shillings. Assuming that the whole batch could be made quickly – within a week, let us say – then he will have to pay for materials, labour and services for all 10,000, which means an investment of 10,000 shillings or £500. This sum will, of course, be gradually repaid during the year as the goods are sold, but the average balance outstanding will be £250, on which the company's bankers will charge interest at, say, 8 per cent per annum, amounting to £20. This investment cost is one we have not previously considered.

If the batch were only half as big, the investment cost would be only £10 a year, but the cost per piece would go up to 1·02 shillings. We therefore have two conflicting goals to reconcile, because economy of scale is only achieved at the expense of a greater investment of capital. How do we reconcile them?

The mathematician will generalize the problem in the following way. Let the batch size which it is required to find be q items and the annual sales be s. Then

Number of batches per year $= s/q$

Let the fixed setting-up cost be f; multiplying this by the number of batches gives the total setting-up costs incurred in a year, which we shall call c. Then

$$c = \frac{fs}{q} \qquad (9.6)$$

For Pascal's Pressings, $s = 10,000$ and $f = 100$ shillings so

$$c = \frac{1,000,000}{q}$$

The variable cost of an item is m; the initial investment for q items is mq and the average balance outstanding is half this. If the rate of interest is r (expressed as a fraction, i.e. $0 \cdot 08$ instead of 8%), then the annual cost of the investment, i, is given by

$$i = \frac{mrq}{2} \qquad (9.7)$$

For Pascal's Pressings, with $m = 1$ and $r = 0 \cdot 08$

$$i = 0 \cdot 04q$$

The direct manufacturing cost per year, g, is given by a simple linear function which does not depend on the batch size:

$$g = ms \qquad (9.8)$$

and by collecting together the costs in equations (9.6), (9.7) and (9.8) we arrive at a total annual cost C:

$$C = c + i + g = \frac{fs}{q} + \frac{mrq}{2} + ms \qquad (9.9)$$

Exercise 9.2

Draw up a table of the following form for the case of Pascal's Pressings, using pounds sterling as the unit instead of shillings.

Number of Pieces in Batch q	Annual Costs, £			Total Annual Cost £ C
	Setting Up c	Investment i	Manufacturing g	
1,000				

Use a range of batch sizes from 1,000 to 10,000 at intervals of 1,000 and set up an equation relating C and q, as an aid to calculation.

Exercise 9.3

If you were the Production Manager, which batch size would you choose and why?

ECONOMIC BATCH SIZE

Figure 9.6 shows how the various components of the total cost vary with the batch size: (it corresponds to the solution of Exercise 9.2). The direct manufacturing cost g has been included in the vertical scale on the right-hand side of the graph, but since it does not vary with the size of batch, only the total $c + i$ need be considered: it is shown on the left-hand scale. The lowest value of $c + i$ is £20, corresponding to

$c + i$ (left-hand scale)

$c + i + g = C$ (right-hand scale)

$$C = \frac{fs}{q} + \frac{mrq}{2} + ms$$

£ — annual costs c and i

q = size of batch

total annual cost C

Fig. 9.6 Economic batch size

5,000 pieces: the latter is known as the 'economic batch size': it represents the best balance between the two conflicting goals of achieving economies of scale and keeping investment costs down.

The question now arises, 'Must we necessarily draw a graph to find the economic batch size – is there not an algebraic method of finding it?' There is such a method, but in order to understand it we shall need to look rather more closely at gradients of curves, which correspond to the rates at which one variable changes with respect to another.

Exercise 9.4

If the batch size q is increased by 1,000, to what extent do the setting-up cost c and the investment cost i change if the increase in batch size is from

    (a) 1,000 to 2,000?
    (b) 4,000 to 5,000?
    (c) 9,000 to 10,000?

RATES OF CHANGE

One characteristic of a linear function is that the rate at which one variable changes with respect to another is always the same: this is the same as saying that the graph of such a function has a constant gradient. In Figure 9.7, the right-

Fig. 9.7 Variation of investment cost with batch size

angled triangles will all have the same ratio between the
vertical and horizontal sides. We called this the gradient m
in Chapter 3, but here we shall describe it in a different way.
The Greek letter delta (Δ) in Figure 9.7 does not represent
a quantity, but is a sign which means 'the difference between
two values of —'. In the black triangle, Δi is the difference
between £10 and £8, i.e. £2, (40 shillings); Δq is the difference between 5,000 and 4,000, i.e. 1,000. The gradient m is
given by

$$m = \frac{\Delta i}{\Delta q} = \frac{40}{1000} = 0.04 \text{ shillings per piece}$$

and for a linear function it is the same no matter where we
draw the triangle, and no matter how large it is: the big
shaded triangle has

$$\Delta i = £18 - £10 = £8 = 160 \text{ shillings}$$

$$\Delta q = 9000 - 5000 \qquad = 4000 \text{ pieces}$$

$$m = \frac{\Delta i}{\Delta q} = \frac{160}{4000} \qquad = 0.04 \text{ shillings per piece}$$

If we want to find the gradient at a point rather than over a
range of values, we can reduce the size of the triangle until it
becomes vanishingly small, knowing that the ratio $m = \dfrac{\Delta i}{\Delta q}$
will not change.

A different notation is used for such infinitesimally small
triangles: we write

$$m = \frac{dc}{dq} \qquad\qquad (9.10)$$

Once again, the symbol 'd' does not denote a quantity, but
means 'an infinitesimally small part of . . .': we cannot cancel
out the d's in equation (9.10).

The gradient $\dfrac{di}{dq}$ is called 'the rate of change of i with respect
to q' or, more technically, 'the first differential coefficient of i
with respect to q'.

DIFFERENTIAL COEFFICIENTS OF
NON-LINEAR FUNCTIONS

A glance at Figure 9.8 will show that the gradient varies at different points along non-linear functions.

It follows that triangles of different sizes enclosing a point on the curve will give different estimates for the gradient at that point. Thus, the big unshaded triangle gives

Fig. 9.8 Variation of setting-up cost with batch size

$$\frac{\Delta c}{\Delta q} = \frac{50 - 10}{1000 - 5000} = \frac{40}{-4000} = -0.01$$

The shaded triangle gives

$$\frac{\Delta c}{\Delta q} = \frac{20 - 14.3}{2500 - 3500} = \frac{5.7}{-1000} = -0.0057$$

The black triangle gives

$$\frac{\Delta c}{\Delta q} = \frac{17.857 - 15.625}{2800 - 3200} = \frac{2.232}{-400} = -0.00558$$

An almost vanishingly small triangle would give

$$\frac{\Delta c}{\Delta q} = \frac{-0.0111}{2} = -0.00555$$

These values approach nearer and nearer to some true value of the gradient at the point $q = 3,000$.

The branch of mathematics known as the differential calculus enables us to calculate the gradient (or rate of change) directly. To explain it in detail would take us beyond the scope of this book; it is sufficient to say here that it reproduces in algebraic form the calculations we have just carried out on Figure 9.8. (A simple explanation of the differential calculus is to be found in *Mathematician's Delight* (1943) by Sawyer.[74])

For instance, the gradient at any point on the graph of

$$i = 50,000/q$$

is shown by the calculus to be

$$di/dq = -50,000/q^2 \qquad (9.10)$$

from which we can confirm that when q is 3,000, the gradient is -0.00555. In other words, the setting-up cost is decreasing at the rate of 0.00555 shillings for every extra part made.

Exercise 9.5

What is the rate of change of investment cost when the batch size is

        (a) 5,000?
        (b) 10,000?

The differential calculus has given us standard methods of calculating rates of change for simple equations, and some of them are given below:

$$\text{If} \qquad y = a \text{ (constant)} \qquad \frac{dy}{dx} = 0 \qquad (9.11)$$

$$y = x \qquad \frac{dy}{dx} = 1 \qquad (9.12)$$

$$y = ax \qquad \frac{dy}{dx} = a \qquad (9.13)$$

$$y = x^2 \qquad \frac{dy}{dx} = 2x \qquad (9.14)$$

$$y = ax^2 \qquad \frac{dy}{dx} = 2ax \qquad (9.15)$$

$$y = \frac{a}{x} \qquad \frac{dy}{dx} = \frac{-a}{x^2} \qquad (9.16)$$

There is also a useful rule that when a function contains two or more terms which are added (or subtracted), they may be differentiated separately and added (or subtracted).

For example,

$$\text{if} \qquad y = x^2 + ax, \qquad dy/dx = 2x + a.$$

Exercise 9.6

Differentiate, i.e. find $\frac{dy}{dx}$ when y equals

(i) $3x$

(ii) 16

(iii) $3x + 16$

(iv) $\frac{1}{x}$

(v) $\frac{a}{x} + bx^2$

(vi) $\frac{a}{x} + bx + ms$

The final example in Exercise 9.6 is similar to equation (9.9). The last term in this equation is constant and its differential coefficient is equal to zero. Putting

$$a = fs \quad \text{and} \quad b = \frac{mr}{2},$$

$$\frac{dC}{dq} = -\frac{a}{q^2} + b$$

$$= -\frac{fs}{q^2} + \frac{mr}{2} \tag{9.17}$$

MINIMA

Look at the top curve in Figure 9.6. At the point $q = 5,000$, $c = 520$ it reaches a lowest point. This is technically called a 'minimum' because the values of C rise on both sides of it.

The minimum corresponds to a point at which, since the curve is flat, its gradient $\frac{dC}{dq}$ is zero, so from equation (9.17) we have

$$-\frac{fs}{q^2} + \frac{mr}{2} = 0 \tag{9.18}$$

i.e

$$\frac{fs}{q^2} = \frac{mr}{2} \tag{9.19}$$

from which it follows that

$$q^2 = \frac{2fs}{mr}$$

and

$$q = \sqrt{\frac{2fs}{mr}} \tag{9.20}$$

Exercise 9.7

Substitute the values

$$f = £5$$
$$s = 10,000 \text{ per annum}$$
$$m = £0\cdot05$$
$$r = 0\cdot08 \text{ per annum}$$

in equation (9.20) and find q.

Exercise 9.8

Multiply both sides of equation (9.19) by q, and compare the result with equations (9.6) and (9.7). What conclusion do you reach?

SENSITIVITY

Common sense should never be far around the corner when mathematical methods are being used in management problems, and sensitivity checks are one way of applying it. The possible inaccuracies in the original data are measured and their effect on the final answer are deduced; we can then judge the sensitivity of the answer to such errors, assess its reliability and, if necessary, try to re-measure the original data with greater accuracy. For example, the economic batch size in this case is associated with a total annual cost of £520 (see Figure 9.6). Of this total, £500 is beyond our control, being fixed by the supplier, but the other £20 is the cost figure we can alter by varying the batch size. In this sense, a batch of 3,650 would cost £21, so a reduction of 27% in the batch size only increases the cost by 5%. A batch of 6,850, 37% greater than the economic batch size, also increases the cost by only 5%. The cost is not 'sensitive' to the batch size, and the latter may therefore be adjusted cheaply in cases where it may be convenient to depart slightly from the true economic level.

PROFITS, PRICES AND PARABOLAS

One view of maximum profit was put forward in the chapters on linear programming. An important assumption was made but not explicitly stated – prices and profit margins remained constant whatever the quantity of goods made and sold might be. Is such an assumption justified?

The classical economists argued otherwise. Under 'perfect' competition, they said, the 'rational entrepreneur' would always buy from the cheapest source, so a lower price would always cause greater sales. Putting this theory into the simplest terms – a linear function – we may write

$$q = a - ep \qquad (9.21)$$

with

$$q = \text{quantity sold}$$
$$a = \text{constant}$$
$$-e = \text{gradient}$$
$$p = \text{selling price}$$

A linear function of this sort is not likely to be valid over a very wide range of s, and would usually be qualified by limits in the usual way

$$p_1 \leqq p \leqq p_2$$

with p_2 and p_1 representing the upper and lower limits of validity respectively.

The gradient $-e$ is, of course, the rate of change of quantity sold with price,

$$\frac{dq}{dp} = -e$$

and has a negative sign because it is reasonable to assume that sales will go up as the price goes down. The quantity 'e' is related to the economist's 'elasticity of demand'.

One should stop and think very carefully about this set of assumptions before charging ahead and applying them. On the one hand, the appeal to elasticity is evident in any retail outlet with price reductions, 'special offers' or trading stamps; it has given rise to the fierce arguments about Retail Price Maintenance and the dilemma of those supporters of a competitive economy who attempt to eliminate the effects of free competition. On the other hand, buying is a complex process of decision-making in which price is only one factor. The wary customer is suspicious of too low a price: one furniture manufacturer has told of a new type of chair, whose revolutionary design kept the cost, and therefore the price, extraordinarily low. 'We couldn't sell it until we put the price up – they just wouldn't believe there wasn't a catch somewhere'. The same phenomenon has been noticed in certain 'quality' newspapers, where an increase in price has led to higher sales.

Other manufacturers go out of their way to persuade people that they are not in a free market. Peas, petrol or pork-pies are assigned 'plus-values', the alleged differences from competitors' products making a direct comparison of prices impossible.

With this caveat, let us follow up the implications of elasticity. If the total sales revenue is R, then

$$R = pq \qquad (9.22)$$

Substituting equation (9.21) gives

$$R = p(a - ep)$$
i.e. $$R = ap - ep^2 \qquad (9.23)$$

The total sales revenue is not a linear function of the price, but a *quadratic* one because it contains p^2.

Exercise 9.9

A supermarket sells peas at the normal market price of 1s. 8d. a tin, and disposes of 1,200 tins weekly. The manager estimates that for every penny by which the price is reduced, sales will increase by 120 tins a week. The lowest possible price is 1/–, which is what the supermarket pays the wholesaler.

(a) What are the values of a and e in the equation (9.21)?
(b) Draw up a table showing the weekly sales and sales revenue for a range of prices from 1/- to 1/8d. at intervals of 1d.
(c) Draw a graph of sales revenue against price.

Suppose that the spacing pieces made by Pascal's Pressings will sell at the rate of 6,000 a week when the price is sixpence (0·50 shillings) and at only 1,000 a week if the price is 1 shilling, with a linear relationship in between. Then

$$q = 11,000 - 10,000p \qquad (9.24)$$
and $$R = 11,000p - 10,000p^2 \qquad (9.25)$$
$$0·50 \leqq p \leqq 1·00$$

The graph of equation (9.25) is shown in Figure 9.9. It shows how sales revenue rises steeply as the price is lowered, reaches a maximum at a price of 0·55 shillings per piece and then begins to fall off. For prices below 0·55, the loss in profit outweighs the growth in sales, the reverse being the case for

Fig. 9.9 Law of diminishing returns

prices above this figure. This is the 'Law of Diminishing Returns', which is in the mind of every Chancellor of the Exchequer before Budget Day. If he raises the tax on beer or cigarettes, can he be sure that the total revenue will increase?

The curve in Figure 9.9 is a *parabola*. The general equation of a parabola is

$$y = k + mx + nx^2 \qquad (9.26)$$

and in equation (9.25),

$$y = R, \qquad x = p,$$
$$k = 0, \qquad m = 11{,}000 \quad \text{and} \quad n = -10{,}000.$$

Every parabola has a point on it at which a maximum or

minimum occurs: if we differentiate equation (9.26) (see equations (9.11) to (9.16)) we find that

$$\frac{dy}{dx} = m + 2nx \qquad (9.27)$$

and the differential coefficient is zero when

$$m + 2nx = 0$$

i.e. when

$$x = \frac{-m}{2n} \qquad (9.28)$$

If x is to have a positive value, then m and n must have different signs.

For the maximum value of R in equation (9.25)

$$p = \frac{11,000}{20,000} = 0 \cdot 55$$

as Figure 9.9 shows.

Exercise 9.10

Calculate the price at which sales revenue is a maximum for the data in Exercise 9.9. Check your result against the graph.

We now know how to fix the price which will maximize sales revenue if (and it is a big 'if') we have some idea of the elasticity. This may well be too simple a view: maximum sales revenue only means maximum profit when costs are constant, whereas we know that increased sales may lead to economies of scale. In Exercise 3.6, we said that the spacing pieces made by Pascal's Pressings had the following cost function:

$$C = 600 + 0 \cdot 25q \qquad (9.29)$$

which is a special case of the more general equation:

$$C = f + vq \qquad (9.30)$$

in which f and v are the fixed and variable costs respectively. The gross profit B is given by

$$\begin{aligned} B &= R - C \\ &= (ap - ep^2) - f - v(a - ep) \end{aligned}$$

which simplifies to

$$B = -ep^2 + (a + ev)p - (av + f) \qquad (9.31)$$

Differentiating gives, for a maximum,

$$\frac{dB}{dp} = -2ep + (a + ev) = 0$$

and therefore

$$p = \frac{a + ev}{2e} \qquad (9.32)$$

It is interesting to note that the fixed cost f does not affect the price at which profit is maximized.

Exercise 9.11

Use equation (9.32) to calculate the 'optimum' price for spacing pieces made by Pascal's Pressings.

Exercise 9.12

Draw up a table of p, q, R, C and B for the spacing pieces, using values of p

(a) from 0·50 to 1·00 inclusive at intervals of 0·10.
(b) for any further values which the results might suggest.

How sensitive is the gross profit to changes in the price?

HOPF'S PARABOLAS

Harry Arthur Hopf formed one of the earliest management consultancy companies in the U.S.A., and propagated a good deal of sound business sense in his teachings. In mathematical analysis, he had a weakness for parabolas; he spent much of his time fitting them to observed data and calculating the corresponding 'optima'.[75] The weakness of Hopf's arguments lies in the fact that other curves (such as logarithmic ones) could have been fitted with equal validity, and would *not* have shown maxima or minima. Hopf's work is of historic interest to the student of management, but some of his conclusions should not be accepted too readily.

For example, in his work on insurance companies, he fitted a parabola to data for ten companies. The administrative expense as a percentage of actuarial net premiums was made the dependent variable y, and the average executive experience, in years, of the major executives was the independent variable x. Hopf fitted his parabola presumably by the method of least squares and found the equation to be

$$y = 19 \cdot 15 - 0 \cdot 5257x + 0 \cdot 014x^2 \qquad (9.33)$$

He then went on to say that

the turn of the curve is clearly defined at the point indicating an average of twenty years of executive experience.

The two exercises which follow show how tenuous this evidence is, and other criticisms may be directed at Hopf's approach. For instance, is it reasonable to assume that executive experience is the only assignable cause of variations in administrative expense?

Exercise 9.13

Comment on Hopf's deduction from his equation by differentiating it and finding the value of x for which y has a minimum value.

Exercise 9.14

Carry out a sensitivity test by calculating values of y corresponding to $x = 15$, 20 and 25. Bearing in mind that the estimate of administrative expense could easily be in error by 1 unit either way, would you attach much importance to executive experience as a factor which influenced it?

SUMMARY

We have seen in this chapter that some managerial problems need to be described in terms of hyperbolas or parabolas as well as straight lines. Logarithmic curves are also useful and so, in some special cases, are those of the simple trigonometrical functions. We rarely need to use more difficult equations than these, because usually our management information is not precise enough to make such elaborations worth while.

Finding maxima or minima by drawing graphs is simple but time-consuming, and the process of differentiating and equating to zero provides rapid solutions to problems of minimizing cost or maximizing profit. It follows that the elements of the differential calculus ought to be far more widely known among managers, accountants and other managerial advisers.

9
Solutions to Exercises

Exercise 9.1

Exercise 9.2

Number of Pieces in Batch q	Annual Costs, £			Total Annual Cost £ C
	Setting up c	Investment i	Manufacturing g	
1,000	50	2	500	552
2,000	25	4	500	529
3,000	16·7	6	500	522·7
4,000	12·5	8	500	520·5
5,000	10·0	10	500	520
6,000	8·3	12	500	520·3
7,000	7·1	14	500	521·1
8,000	6·2	16	500	522·2
9,000	5·6	18	500	523·6
10,000	5·0	20	500	525

$$C = c + i + g$$
$$= \frac{50,000}{q} + 0{\cdot}002q + 500$$

Exercise 9.3

Presumably you would choose a batch size of 5,000 because the total cost would then be at its lowest.

Exercise 9.4

Change in batch size		*Change in cost of*	
from	*to*	*Setting up*	*Investment*
1,000	2,000	−£25	+£2
4,000	5,000	−£2·5	+£2
9,000	10,000	−£0·6	+£2

Exercise 9.5

$$\text{(a)} - \frac{50,000}{(5,000)^2} = -0.0020$$

$$\text{(b)} - \frac{50,000}{(10,000)^2} = -0.0005$$

Exercise 9.6

$$\text{(i)} \quad 3$$

$$\text{(ii)} \quad 0$$

$$\text{(iii)} \quad 3$$

$$\text{(iv)} \quad -\frac{1}{x^2}$$

$$\text{(v)} \quad -\frac{a}{x^2} + 2bx$$

$$\text{(vi)} \quad -\frac{a}{x^2} + b$$

Exercise 9.7

$$q = \sqrt{\frac{2 \times 5 \times 10,000}{0.05 \times 0.08}} = 5,000 \text{ (refer back to Ex. 9.3)}$$

Exercise 9.8

$$\frac{fs}{q} = \frac{mrq}{2}$$

$$\text{i.e. } c = i$$

The conclusion reached is that the annual investment and setting-up costs are equal when the batch size has the value which gives minimum total cost. Check that this is so by studying Figure 9.6.

Exercise 9.9

(a)

$$e = 120 \text{ tins per penny reduction.}$$

$$\text{therefore } q = a - 120p, \qquad 12 \leqq p \leqq 20$$

$$\text{and } a = q + 120p$$

$$\text{When } p = 20, \qquad q = 1200$$

$$a = 1200 + 120 \times 20 = 3600.$$

(b)

Price (*pence*) p	Sales (*tins*) q	Revenue (*pence*) pq
20	1,200	24,000
19	1,320	25,080
18	1,440	25,920
17	1,560	26,520
16	1,680	26,880
15	1,800	27,000
14	1,920	26,880
13	2,040	26,520
12	2,160	25,920

Exercise 9.10

$$R = 3,600p - 120p^2$$

$$\frac{dR}{dp} = 3,600 - 240p = 0$$

$$\therefore p = \frac{3,600}{240} = 15$$

This value of p corresponds to the maximum revenue (27,000) in Exercise 9.9.

Exercise 9.11

$$a = 11,000$$
$$e = 10,000$$
$$v = 0 \cdot 25$$
$$\therefore p = 0 \cdot 675 \text{ shillings.}$$

Exercise 9.12

p	q	R	C	B
0·50	6,000	3,000	2,100	900
0·60	5,000	3,000	1,850	1,150
0·70	4,000	2,800	1,600	1,200
0·80	3,000	2,400	1,350	1,050
0·90	2,000	1,800	1,100	700
1·00	1,000	1,000	850	150

Further values of p give

0·65	4,500	2,925	1,725	1,200
0·66	4,400	2,904	1,700	1,204
0·67	4,300	2,881	1,675	1,206
0·68	4,200	2,856	1,650	1,206
0·69	4,100	2,829	1,625	1,204
0·675	4,250	2,868·75	1,662·50	1,206·25

A change of 0·005 in the price, up or down, makes a difference of 0·25 shillings in the gross profit: this is trivially small.

Exercise 9.13

$$y = 19·15 - 0·5257x + 0·014x^2$$

$$\frac{dy}{dx} = -0·5257 + 0·028x = 0$$
$$\text{for a minimum}$$

$$\therefore \quad x = \frac{0·5257}{0·028} = 19 \text{ years.}$$

Hopf has obviously rounded off this result to obtain his figure of 20 years.

Exercise 9.14

$$x = 15, \quad y = 14·4$$
$$x = 20, \quad y = 14·2$$
$$x = 25, \quad y = 14·8$$

It is obvious that y is not very sensitive to changes in x.

NOTES AND REFERENCES

73 Garvin, W. W., Crandall, H. W., John, J. B., and Spellman, R. A., *Management Science* (1957), p. 407.

74 Sawyer, W. W., *Mathematician's Delight* (Penguin Books, 1967).

75 Hopf, H. A., *Management and the Optimum* (6th International Congress for Scientific Management, 1935). Quoted in Merrill, H. F., *Classics in Management*, p. 355 (American Management Association, 1960).

Statistics and Sundries

Lest men suspect your tale to be untrue,
Keep probability – some say – in view.

ROBERT GRAVES, *The Devil's Advice to Story-Tellers*

STATISTICAL METHODS[76]

The preceding chapters have surveyed some of the mathematical procedures which can help the modern manager to solve his problems, but they have necessarily omitted many others. Foremost among the omissions are the methods of mathematical statistics which have been derived from the theory of probability. Some mathematicians will argue that 'statistics' is not included in mathematics and imply that there is something rather disreputable about the whole basis of probability theory. Perhaps this is another aspect of the Snobbery of Purity, for of the practical value of statistical methods there can be no doubt. They have led to improvements in many fields where human welfare is affected (medicine, agriculture, psychology and sociology among them) and where random effects obtrude. The highly variable conditions of real life make it difficult for investigators to detect the effects of new drugs, new fertilizers and new methods of treatment as soon as they move outside the carefully controlled conditions of the laboratory: no two patients are exactly alike in their response to a drug, no two fields have the same soil. A crop growing in a field treated with a new fertilizer may have different weather from a 'control' crop without it, and so on. Statistical methods help the investigator to decide, in spite of the fog of uncertainty, whether the new drug or fertilizer really is effective. The old saying, 'You can prove anything by statistics', is wrong, for no statistician can ever produce a hard and fast proof of anything. He deals with the balance of probabilities, and his 'proof' will take some such form as, 'Either this new drug works, or you have a freak result with odds of 250 to one against a repetition'.

So also in management, for the man who works in industry is constantly beset by outside interference. How, for example, can a food manufacturer assess the state of his market? Each individual customer is a creature of whims and fancies: if he himself does not know which foods he means to buy next week, how can the manufacturer predict his behaviour? He can only do so in the vaguest terms, but it is a remarkable fact that the behaviour of large numbers of people is much more predictable than that of the individuals themselves. The Ministry of Food in Britain during the Second World War was able to predict the food requirements of the whole population within narrow limits, and plan not only a basic food ration but also a 'points' system which would enable each consumer to adjust his personal intake.

MARKET RESEARCH[77]

Aggregate effects of this sort begin to appear when the 'large numbers' are still relatively small. Six hundred is a large number of people, but it is still only 0·001% of a total population of sixty million. Nevertheless, by studying the behaviour, characteristics, or opinions of this small fraction, a researcher can often draw useful conclusions about the corresponding factors in the whole population. This is the basic idea of market research, and statistical methods can help in assessing the limits of reliability of the results. By the skilful use of such methods, the sample can be chosen so that the limits are as narrow as is possible for the size of the survey – in other words, so that the sample is 'representative'.

STOCK CONTROL[78]

Another important application of statistical methods is in controlling stocks of materials during manufacture and distribution. A manufacturer may find that, although his sales in any one month are not perfectly predictable, a statistical analysis of his previous sales over several months will yield useful data. An 'expected value' of next month's sales can then be deduced and will enable him to prepare his manufacturing programme. The limits of confidence which accompany this figure will be used for calculating the level of reserve stock which he must carry in order to cope with a reasonable range of variation. Some managers have been able, by the use of simple statistical techniques, to reduce the capital tied up in stocks by as much as 40%, with no loss of efficiency or customer service. Moreover, questions such as 'what do we mean by a *reasonable* range of variation?' can lead to profound inquiries into the general management policy of a company.

QUALITY CONTROL[79]

Statistical control of the quality of manufactured goods has been applied in this country for a quarter of a century, but many companies still remain in ignorance of its advantages. Variations in some measure of quality, such as dimensions or the proportion of flawed items, also obey statistical laws; by studying and applying them we can take steps to avoid unnecessary expenditure on inspection, machine supervision, or replacing rejected material; we can also ensure that quality is specified at levels which are a reasonable compromise between what is needed to satisfy the customer and what can be produced at a price he is prepared to pay.

The mathematical theories of statistics may appear complicated to the layman, but this is no excuse for avoiding them. The fundamental concepts, as distinct from their detailed interpretation, are not difficult to understand, and often make an immediate appeal to our common sense or intuition. Tables, special graph papers and rapid statistical methods have taken much of the sting out of the calculations and, of course, the electronic computer can take care of the drudgery of calculation once the methods of working have been decided.

FORECASTING[80]

The art of business forecasting has also been greatly advanced by the work of statisticians. The nineteenth-century biologist Galton developed a method of fitting curves to observed data when he was investigating the relationship between the heights of fathers and their sons. He called it 'regression analysis' and it is now the most widely used method of scientific forecasting. The curves may be linear or may follow some of the curves described in Chapter 9, and the method of analysis permits us not only to project them into the future as expected values but also to work out the limits within which the forecast may be reasonably expected to lie. Simple transformations are often used, as when the sales of a commodity are believed to be increasing by a constant percentage r each year, but with random variations. The latter may make it difficult to estimate the value of r which will give us the best projection of past data. The method is to start with a 'base year' which we call year 0; we denote the sales in that year by s_0. Then the sales in the next year, s_1, will be given by

$$s_1 = s_0(1 + \frac{r}{100}) \qquad (10.1)$$

and the sales in any subsequent year n will be s_n, where

$$s_n = s_0(1 + \frac{r}{100})^n \qquad (10.2)$$

This is the same equation, incidentally, as the one which is used for compound interest, s_0 being the initial sum invested and s_n its value after n years at r per cent interest. To say that sales increase by five per cent every year is the same as saying that they are multiplied by a factor of $1 \cdot 05$, and by using this approach we get a simpler equation. In general terms, we say that the rate of interest, r, is transformed into the multiplier R by the equation

$$R = 1 + \frac{r}{100} \qquad (10.3)$$

which gives, by substitution in (10.2),

$$s_n = s_o R^n \qquad (10.4)$$

We still have the awkward problem of R^n to deal with. Once again we can transform the variables, using that most useful invention, the logarithm. You may remember that if

$$R = 10^c,$$

c is the logarithm of R and, from reasoning which can be found in any elementary textbook,

$$\log R^n = n \log R$$

and this rule indicates how the variables in equation should be transformed.

Taking logarithms throughout gives

$$\begin{aligned} \log s_n &= \log s_o + \log (R^n) \\ &= \log s_o + n\log R \end{aligned} \qquad (10.5)$$

Since s_o is constant, its logarithm is also constant, so we put $\log s_o = c$. We also believe r to have a constant value, so $\log R$ is also constant and we make it equal to m. The independent variable with which we are concerned is n, so let $n = x$. Then the dependent variable, which we shall call Y_n, is defined by the transformation $Y_n = \log s_n$ and we have, by substitution,

$$Y_n = mx + c \qquad (10.6)$$

which is the general equation to a straight line. This bit of mathematical reasoning shows why we so often use semi-log graph paper for projecting sales. An example is given in Figure 10.1, which is a graph showing the rate of growth of the consumption of alkali in Britain, taken over the last sixty years and projected forward to the year 2000. Alkali is a widely used industrial commodity, and it is of interest to compare its average rate of growth ($r = 3.25\%$) with current 'Neddy' targets for the economy as a whole.

There are even more advanced techniques of statistical forecasting, such as 'multiple regression' by which we can relate a dependent variable (for example, sales) not only to a single independent variable, time, but to several of them, such as weather or population.[81] The equations which are used for this

Fig. 10.1 Rate of growth of alkali consumption   *Reproduced by courtesy of I.C.I. Ltd.*

purpose are very like that which described the multi-factor bonus scheme (see Figure 3.6 and equation 3.17).

BRAND LOYALTY AND MARKET SHARES

An even more recent advance has been the use of 'matrices of transition probabilities' for forecasting changes in market shares.[82] A simple matrix for three branded products is shown in Fig. 10.1, the probabilities having been deduced from observation of a small representative panel. In this simple case, we can easily calculate the market share which each brand would have when an equilibrium was reached.

If the market shares of Plankton, Seaweed and Kelp are p, s, and k respectively, then p, s and k will all have constant values when the market is in equilibrium, that is, when all market shares are stable.

For their next purchase, 0·7 of the previous buyers of Plankton will again buy Plankton, 0·1 of the buyers of S will switch to Plankton, and so will 0·2 of the Kelp addicts. A little thought will show that because p remains unchanged,

$$p = 0·7p + 0·1s + 0·2k \tag{10.6}$$

which gives

$$-0·3p + 0·1s + 0·2k = 0 \tag{10.7}$$

A similar operation on s gives

$$0·2p - 0·5s + 0·2k = 0 \tag{10.8}$$

Having tacitly assumed that the three commodities share the whole of the particular market which is being surveyed, we can also write

$$p + s + k = 1 \tag{10.9}$$

We now have three simultaneous equations, which, when solved give

$$
\begin{aligned}
p &= 0·343 \quad (34·3\% \text{ of the market}) \\
s &= 0·286 \quad (28·6\% \text{ ,, ,, ,, }) \\
k &= 0·371 \quad (37·1\% \text{ ,, ,, ,, }) \\
\hline
& 1·000
\end{aligned}
$$

TABLE 10.1

Brand Loyalty: Matrix of Transition Probabilities

If the customer's last purchase was A, then the probability that his next purchase will be B is given in the various cells.

		B (Next purchase)		
		Pythagoras' Processed Plankton	Socrates' Shredded Seaweed	Keltic Kelp Kakes
A (Last pur- chase)	Pythagoras' Processed Plankton	0·7	0·2	0·1
	Socrates' Shredded Seaweed	0·1	0·5	0·4
	Keltic Kelp Kakes	0·2	0·2	0·6

The result is rather surprising, because the highest 'brand loyalty' is towards Pythagoras' Plankton (see the entry 0·7 in Table 10.1), and yet this is not enough to ensure it the highest market share. To some extent, this is due to the seaweed-eaters, who tend to turn to kelp rather than plankton when they switch brands. Here is a way of predicting how market shares may change, instead of having to wait for the results of market audits.

Why have so few manufacturers tried it out? Either because, lacking mathematicians to advise them, they do not know of it – or if they do, the dreadful words 'matrix of transition probabilities' or 'Markov chains' (and the symbols which accompany them) have frightened them away.

COMMUNICATION AND MENTAL WORK

The study of mental work has interested many scientists, from Charles Babbage[83] to the modern workers in cybernetics. The current trend is to use the mathematical theory of communication, developed in the 1930s by Shannon[84,85]. This theory is built up from the idea that the amount of information in a signal depends upon its rarity. You can see this by imagining two incomplete messages in Morse code:

    (a) PLEASE SEND ME A R————
    (b) PLEASE SEND ME A X————

In the first of these, R, being a commonly used letter is said to be a signal with a low information content, and so the message as a whole will have a lower information content than (b) because X is a rarer letter.

The concept of rarity is closely allied to that of probability, and by applying statistical reasoning, Shannon and Weaver succeeded in building up a measure of information. Some rather crude attempts have been made to apply their system of measurement to mental work, which may be defined as the reception, storage and transmission of information. The attempts have been limited by the lack of distinction between information which has *meaning* or *relevance* and that which has not. Recent developments of the theory have interpreted the meaning of the signals in terms of the action which they initiate. (In case (b), one might send off a xylophone and a xerographic machine accompanied by a xenophobe and stand a reasonable chance of having interpreted the meaning correctly.) Devising and applying a numerical measure of 'meaningfulness' may well be one of the great new contributions of mathematics to management in the next decade.

INSPECTION AND INFORMATION

The theory of information has been applied to inspectors looking for faults in glass bottles.[86] Each inspector was looked on as a communication channel with a limited capacity to handle information. The input signals were the flaws detected by the inspector, and his output was the action taken to separate faulty bottles from good ones. For a given frequency of defects, the rate at which information flowed through the 'channel' was obviously proportional to the rate at which the bottles passed along the inspection line. If the information capacity of the channel, that is, the inspector, were exceeded, his *apparent* output would rise because he would appear to inspect more bottles. His *true* output would, however, remain constant because he would make a greater number of mistakes by rejecting good bottles or passing bad ones. Similar work has been done on airline pilots and radar operators.

THE OVERLOADED CONTROLLER

One of the most remarkable applications of statistics to management problems has been described by Lee.[87] His team tackled the problem of the Departures Controller at London Airport, who was thought to be carrying too heavy a load of work. The Controller's job was to keep in touch with more than 20 people who collectively supervised the preparation of an aircraft for take-off: he received their messages, made decisions and passed on instructions. In other words, he worked with his brain rather than his muscles.

A team of investigators from British European Airways built up a measure of the mental work load (not quite the same as Shannon's) and used it to divide up the Departure Controller's job when it became obvious that it took two men to handle it. The obvious division was to allocate the work according to the existing organization, that is, domestic flights to one man and foreign flights to another. The measurements showed that this proposal was inequitable, and a better alternative was found. The work tended to build up into a peak near the scheduled take-off time, and in fact half the total work for each aircraft was concentrated into the last twenty minutes.

The method which was finally devised called for the first Controller to handle each aircraft until twenty minutes before its departure, at which time he handed it over to the second. Lee said of this:

> The division of responsibility would be quite even, because the more serious, because more urgent, snags occur near flight departure. Although Controller A would be dealing with as many as 40 flights at one time, whereas Controller B would not

be concerned with more than about 8, the actual number of calls handled per minute and the number of topics being stored by each in his memory, would be almost the same, and both well below the respective critical levels.

SUMMING UP

This book is presented as a 'shop-window' of mathematical methods and concepts which can be of immediate, practical use to managers. The price they have to pay is the effort to break down the barrier of communication between themselves and the mathematicians. If the simplified descriptions in the preceding chapters have helped to breach this barrier, they will have achieved their objective. And if you, the manager, like the look of what is in the window, why not come inside and see the whole stock? Or if you, the mathematician, find the manager a more interesting and demanding customer than you first thought, why not try serving behind the counter for a while?

NOTES AND REFERENCES

76 Freund, J. E., and Williams, F. J., *Modern Business Statistics* (Pitman, 1959).

77 Schreier, F. T., *Modern Marketing Research* (Wadsworth Publishing Co. Inc., Belmont, Calif., U.S.A., 1963).

78 Battersby, A., *A Guide to Stock Control* (Pitman, 1962).

79 Juran, J. M., *Quality Control Handbook* (2nd edn., McGraw-Hill, 1962).

80 Brown, R. G., *Statistical Forecasting for Inventory Control* (McGraw-Hill, 1959)

81 Snedecor, G. W., *Statistical Methods* (4th edn, p. 133, Iowa State College Press, 1946).

82 Styan, G. P. H., and Smith, H. Jr, *Journal of Marketing Research* (Feb. 1964), p. 50

83 Morrison, P., and Morrison, E. (eds), *Charles Babbage and his Calculating Engines*, Part II, chapter VI, (Dover, 1961).

84 Shannon, C., and Weaver, W., *The Mathematical Theory of Communication* (University of Illinois Press, 1949).

85 Ashby, W. R., *An Introduction to Cybernetics* (Chapman and Hall, 1957).

86 Broadbent, S. R., *Journal of the Royal Statistical Society, Series B* (1958), vol. 20, p. 111.

87 Lee, A. M., *Operational Research Quarterly* (1959), vol. 10, No. 4, p. 206.

GERBIL GENIUS

Ashley

Books in the Animal Ark Pets series

BEN M. BAGLIO

GERBIL GENIUS

Illustrated by
Paul Howard

Cover Illustration by
Chris Chapman

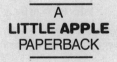

A
LITTLE APPLE
PAPERBACK

SCHOLASTIC INC.

New York Toronto London Auckland Sydney
Mexico City New Delhi Hong Kong

Special thanks to Pat Posner.
Thanks also to C.J. Hall, B.Vet.Med., M.R.C.V.S., for reviewing
the veterinary material contained in this book.

ISBN 0-439-05166-5

Copyright © 1998 by Ben M. Baglio.
Illustrations copyright © 1998 by Paul Howard.

12 11 10 9 8

4 5/0

Printed in the U.S.A.

40

First Scholastic Trade printing, February 2000

Contents

1

Mouse Counting Day

Mandy Hope was standing at her bedroom window listening to the church bells ringing out over Welford village. Her grandpa was one of the bell ringers and Mandy sometimes tried to guess which bell he was ringing.

But today, Mandy was waiting impatiently for the bells to stop. Then she could go and meet Grandpa, her best friend, James Hunter, and his dad, who lived at the other end of the village. The four of them had something very special to do this morning.

Mandy stuck her head further out of the window. The sun was shining, but there was a gentle breeze. She smiled as the wind ruffled her hair. Perfect weather.

Suddenly Mandy heard another sound — a fretful whining coming from the modern building attached to the back of the house. Mandy's parents were both vets at Animal Ark, and the extension was their clinic. The whining was coming from the unit, a special room where animals stayed if they weren't well enough to go home.

That's probably Sasha, Mandy told herself, pulling her head back inside the window. She decided to ask her mom if she could give the dog a quick cuddle.

Dr. Emily Hope was on her way to the clinic when Mandy bounded downstairs. "Can I go and see Sasha, Mom?" asked Mandy, as her mom opened the door that led from the house to the clinic.

"Okay. Just for a minute or two," Dr. Emily replied.

Sasha was an Afghan hound. She'd had a small lump removed from her eyelid. "She'll be going home today," said Dr. Emily. She smiled as she watched Mandy stroking the beautiful dog.

"What about Smudge?" asked Mandy, moving to another large cage where a young black and white cat was pacing restlessly. Smudge had been in a fight with another cat and he had seven stitches in his ear.

"He can go home, too," said Dr. Emily. "I'll call Naomi Bruce in a little while and tell her she can come and get him."

"That's good," said Mandy. "He doesn't like being shut up in this cage. Do you, boy?" Mandy rubbed his nose through the bars. Smudge glared at her and meowed loudly.

"Come on," said Dr. Emily. "We'll leave them to rest now."

They went back into the house and Mandy hurried to the kitchen and ran to the back door. "The bells have stopped," she said. "I can go and meet Grandpa now!"

"Why? Are you going somewhere with him?" asked Dr. Adam Hope as he came into the kitchen.

"Dad! You haven't really forgotten what's happening today, have you?" said Mandy.

"Stop teasing her, Adam," laughed Dr. Emily. "You know why Mandy's meeting Grandpa."

"And James and his dad," Mandy said happily.

Dr. Adam smiled and pointed to the calendar on the kitchen wall. Next to today's date Mandy had written the words **MOUSE COUNTING DAY** in big red letters. "I couldn't really forget what you're doing today, could I?" he chuckled. "Off you go, and good luck."

"Don't forget to take the mixed seed," said Dr. Emily, pointing to two brown paper bags on the kitchen table.

"Thanks, Mom." Mandy picked them up. "I'll see you both later," she said and hurried off.

The others were waiting for her outside the general store.

"I thought you were never going to get here, Mandy," said James when she raced up to them. "My dad and I have been here for ages."

"I went into the unit to see Sasha and Smudge," puffed Mandy as she hugged Grandpa. "It must have taken longer than I thought."

Mr. Hunter smiled. "Don't pay any attention to James, Mandy. We've only been here a couple of minutes. We arrived at the same time as your grandpa."

"Well, it seemed like ages to me," said James, pushing his glasses further on to the bridge of his nose.

They turned on to the narrow street at the side of the general store. This was a shortcut to the river. As they hurried along, they saw Mrs. Ponsonby walking toward them. She lived in Bleakfell Hall, a huge gray stone house on the outskirts of Welford. Mrs. Ponsonby often came to the village; she liked to keep an eye on what was happening there.

Mrs. Ponsonby was wearing a large straw hat with poppies around the brim and a white dress with a pattern of blue, red, yellow, and orange flowers all over it.

"She looks like a flower shop," James whispered to Mandy.

Mandy nodded and smiled. Mrs. Ponsonby always seemed to wear colorful clothes and big hats. Then Mandy noticed Pandora, Mrs. Ponsonby's plump Pekingese. Pandora was wearing a straw hat, too!

"The poor little darling gets so hot," said Mrs. Ponsonby when she saw Mandy looking at the hat. "She begged so hard to go for a walk along the riverbank that I put her sun hat on so she wouldn't get sunstroke."

"Good morning, Mr. Hope, Mr. Hunter," she added as Grandpa and James's dad got close. "You'll never guess what someone has done to the reed beds!"

Mrs. Ponsonby didn't wait for a reply. She continued indignantly, "Someone has dumped loads of old tennis balls there. It's a disgrace, that's what it is. I'm going to report it to the council first thing tomorrow and have them removed."

Mandy and James gazed at each other in dismay. Then Mandy blurted out, "You didn't *do* anything to the tennis balls, did you, Mrs. Ponsby? You see, *we* put the tennis balls there. I mean some of us from school put them there."

"They're special feeding houses," added James. "The balls have little holes in one side for a door and we slotted a bamboo cane through two slits on the back of each ball."

"Then we stuck the canes upright into the ground and put some mixed seed inside each mouse house," said Mandy. "And —"

"*Mouse* house?" interrupted Mrs. Ponsonby.

Mandy almost giggled. She thought Mrs. Ponsonby had sounded just like a mouse herself.

Then Grandpa explained that Mandy and James's school was taking part in a survey to find out how common harvest mice were in different areas all over the country.

"In some parts of the country, farmers grow more than one crop of hay or wheat a year," said James. "That means they're cutting the hay and wheat down just at the time the harvest mice want to build their nests. The survey will help us find out if the mice have found different places to live."

"We put fifty mouse houses in the reed beds

on Friday," said Mandy. "Today we're going to check how many have been used. It's our first mouse counting day!"

"You mean you're going to look inside each house and see if there's a mouse there?" shuddered Mrs. Ponsonby.

Mandy shook her head. "We're going to look inside and see if the seeds we put there have been eaten," she explained. "If they have, it will mean a harvest mouse has eaten them, because the little hole is too small for other creatures to use. Then we'll *know* there are harvest mice here. It will be great if we do find a mouse in a house," she added. "But I don't think we will."

"I still think the tennis balls are a bit of an eyesore," said Mrs. Ponsonby. "But," she added, giving a small bow, "seeing as you're carrying out a survey, I won't ask to have them removed."

"Whew!" breathed James as they watched Mrs. Ponsonby totter away on her high-heeled shoes. "Good thing we explained it all. It would have been awful if she'd done something to get our mouse houses taken away."

"Well, it's all settled now," said Grandpa. "Let's get a move on it and do some counting," he added, smiling down at his granddaughter.

A little while later, Mandy and James had worked their way along one row of mouse houses. Grandpa and Mr. Hunter were working their way along another row. "Eight of the houses along this row are empty," she said, beaming. "That means something has eaten the seed. Right, James?"

James nodded happily. "Yes," he said, popping some more seed through a small hole in one of the empty houses.

Mr. Hunter told them he and Mr. Hope had found five empty houses on their row.

"That means . . ." Mandy did a quick count, ". . . thirteen out of twenty-two mouse houses have been used."

"But," James worked a sum out in his head, "there are still twenty-eight mouse houses to check!"

"How can anyone really figure out how many harvest mice are here?" asked Mr. Hunter. "It might just be one eating all the seeds."

"That mouse would be a happy, *fat* one, Dad!" said James. Then he added, "Our teachers, Mrs. Black and Mrs. Todd, said we won't be able to figure *that* out correctly."

Mandy nodded. "They said that part of it will have to be guesswork. They said we should count three empty houses as one harvest mouse."

"But the main thing," James stated, "is that we know for sure that there *are* harvest mice here."

"Come on, then, let's start on the next row!" Mandy hurried over and bent down in front of a mouse house. The cane was quite tall, but the tennis ball house was only about nineteen inches from the ground.

Mandy carefully pulled the little house off its bamboo cane. She held it in one hand and shook it over the palm of her other. "No seed left in this one!" she said to James.

She replaced the tennis ball and walked a few steps to get some seed. The houses were about forty inches apart. She and James were sharing one bag of seed and Grandpa and Mr. Hunter were sharing the other. "We'll have to tell the others to bring a small bag of seed *each*," Mandy said. "It won't take us long then."

"Good idea," agreed James. "I don't need any for this house, though, there's still lots of seed in it." He put the house back and walked on, leaving the next mouse house he passed for Mandy to check.

Suddenly Grandpa appeared behind the mouse house Mandy was about to check. "I'm sure I heard a noise coming from inside this one," he whispered, bending down.

"You mean there's a mouse inside?" Mandy said excitedly.

Grandpa nodded. "I think there could be!" he said.

2

A Big Surprise

Mandy knelt down to listen and her eyes widened as she heard a strange little thumping noise. It lasted for only a second, but she *knew* she'd heard it. Maybe a harvest mouse was building a nest inside the feeding house. Mrs. Todd, her teacher, had said that might happen, because the tennis balls were almost the same size and shape as a harvest mouse's nest.

Mandy signaled to James, then shuffled along on her knees, edging herself closer to the mouse house. She was trying really hard to move silently, but the tops of her shoes brushed some reeds and they rustled slightly. Mandy froze and glanced at James as the thumping noise from inside the mouse house started again.

"Wow!" breathed James, his eyes shining with excitement.

"If that's a harvest mouse it must be wearing shoes to make that sort of noise!" said Grandpa.

James and Mandy listened to the drumming noise and stared at the tennis ball mouse house. Then James pointed to the door hole. "See that, Mandy? The hole's been made bigger."

"The harvest mouse probably made it bigger so it could carry nesting material in," Mandy whispered. "Maybe the mouse is planning to cover the hole with leaves and grass from the inside. Oh, I wish we could peep in, but that might frighten it and make it run off."

"Let's just watch for a while," James suggested. "It might come out if it thinks we've gone. Then it would be safe to look in."

Mandy nodded. She hoped the harvest mouse *would* come out. She'd never seen a real live one close up. She'd never seen a harvest mouse's nest, either, other than in photos or on television. Now, she and James might see both. It would be great telling everyone at school about it tomorrow!

Grandpa and Mr. Hunter finished off the mouse house count on their own, while James and Mandy sat with their eyes glued to the door hole of the tennis ball.

After a while, they returned and crouched down beside Mandy and James.

Grandpa said quietly, "We've added all the figures up and, altogether, twenty-eight houses are being used."

"Over half. That's great!" Mandy exclaimed.

"I've written it down in the notebook for you, James," Mr. Hunter told him.

"Thanks, Dad," whispered James. "I think Mandy and I will stay here a while if that's okay."

"We want to know if the harvest mouse is nesting in there," said Mandy. "We'll come home as soon as we find out."

Another half an hour went by before anything happened. Then a face appeared at the door hole. It was a dark golden color and, for a moment, two big, round, dark eyes stared unblinkingly at Mandy and James. The creature's ears were standing straight up, its brown nose and long whiskers were twitching. Then the face disappeared.

Startled, Mandy and James gazed at each other. They'd only seen the creature for a second or two, but they both knew it definitely *wasn't* a harvest mouse!

"It's a gerbil!" Mandy whispered. "Oh, James, the poor little thing must have gotten out of its cage and made its way outside. Gerbils can't survive out of doors in this country, can they? We'll have to take it to Animal Ark."

James nodded. "But we'd better not try to get it out," he whispered back. "It might escape again. We'll have to carry it there in the mouse house, Mandy."

They got quietly to their feet and tiptoed closer to the tennis ball. They heard the gerbil give a frightened squeak, then they saw its face at the door hole again. As quick as a flash, James darted forward and put both hands around the tennis ball, covering the door hole with the palm of one hand.

"Good job," said Mandy with a relieved smile. "It would have been awful if it had gotten away!"

Keeping the ball clasped firmly between his hands, James straightened up and eased the ball off the cane. "Let's go," he said with a triumphant smile.

As they hurried off to Animal Ark, Mandy couldn't help wondering about the gerbil they had found. They had two pet gerbils in her class at school and Mrs. Todd had told them that gerbils burrowed. Mandy wondered why this gerbil had gone into the mouse house instead of tunneling and making itself a burrow.

"Maybe the soil was too hard or too crumbly for him to dig a burrow," she said aloud.

James nodded and glanced at the ball he was holding tightly in both hands. "I've been thinking about that," he said. "Maybe he did make a burrow somewhere. He might have come out and seen the harvest mice going into the houses and guessed there was food inside."

"He must have been really hungry," said Mandy. "Or . . ." She clapped her hand over her mouth.

"Or what?" James asked urgently.

"Maybe he's sick or hurt and went in the house to hide because he wasn't strong enough to make a burrow!" she said.

There wasn't far to go now. They were both worried that the gerbil might need help, so they walked as fast as they could.

3

A Worrying Time

Dr. Emily was sitting on a lounge chair on the patio, reading the Sunday paper, when Mandy and James arrived at Animal Ark. Mandy flung open the back gate and ran across the lawn, leaving James to follow more slowly with the gerbil.

"Mom!" said Mandy, bounding up onto the patio.

Dr. Emily lowered her newspaper. "Is something wrong?" she asked, seeing Mandy's anxious expression.

Mandy nodded and pointed to James, who was walking toward them with the mouse house clasped firmly between his hands.

"Grandpa said you'd heard noises from inside one of the mouse houses," said Dr. Emily, getting to her feet. "Is it an injured harvest mouse?"

"It's a gerbil, Dr. Emily," said James, looking up with a worried expression.

Dr. Emily glanced doubtfully at the mouse house.

"We *both* saw his face, Mom," said Mandy. "We're really sure it's a gerbil."

"Okay. We'll go and have a look," said Dr. Emily.

"Oh, no," said Dr. Adam as they trooped through the kitchen. "I was just about to make ice-cream sodas. But something tells me this is another animal rescue."

"Could be," Dr. Emily replied. "Mandy and James think there's a gerbil in this mouse house."

As the three of them went into the clinic, Dr. Emily asked Mandy to get a cardboard pet carrier.

James followed Dr. Emily into the treatment room. She put on her white vet's coat, then smiled at James as he rested his cupped hands on the examination table. "I bet your fingers are aching," she said.

James nodded. "I've been keeping them tightly over the door hole in case the gerbil jumps out and gets away," he said. "We heard him squeaking before, but he didn't make any noise all the way here. Do you think he might be sick, Dr. Emily?"

"We'll soon find out, James," Dr. Emily replied as she pulled on a pair of rubber gloves.

Mandy came in with the pet carrier and put it on the table with a puzzled look. She didn't know why her mom wanted such a large box for a gerbil.

When Dr. Emily opened up the carrier she put an empty metal instrument tray in and told James to lower the mouse house to the bottom of the carrier. Then she put her hand over James's. "Okay," she said quietly. "Move your hands away now, James."

James slowly moved his hand from under Dr. Emily's. Then he sighed with relief and wriggled his fingers. But he didn't take his eyes off the mouse house.

"What are you going to do, Mom?" asked Mandy.

"I'm going to tip him into a corner and use the tray as a barrier," Dr. Emily explained. "In case whatever it is tries to jump."

Mandy and James held their breath as Dr. Emily lifted the tennis ball ever so slightly, tilting it so the door hole was facing toward one corner of the carrier.

A small, browny-gold animal slid out, head first. It quickly rose up on its hind legs, curling its smaller front legs and little clawed feet inward under its neck, showing the paler color of its chest and tummy. Although it was the same shape as a mouse, it was a bit bigger.

"It *is* a gerbil!" said Dr. Emily. "I really thought you two had made a mistake," she admitted. "I was expecting a giant harvest mouse to pop out of the mouse house."

For a second the gerbil seemed to be frozen to the spot. Mandy bit her lip. The poor little thing was so scared — its dark chocolate-brown eyes were huge with fright.

Dr. Emily put the ball down gently and very slowly tilted the metal tray. The gerbil lowered its front legs and then, with small, alarmed squeaks, it darted into the corner. It pressed its pointed snout right against the cardboard.

They could see its body trembling and its tail — about the same length as its body — lay straight out behind it, resting on the bottom of the carrier.

The lower half of the gerbil's tail looked really strange — as if the fur had been shaved

off. It was pink and sore-looking, too! Mandy pointed and lifted worried eyes to her mom's face.

Dr. Emily nodded, straightened up, and closed the carrier. "The skin covering his tail has been shed," she explained. "That *can* happen if gerbils are picked up by the end of their tails. In this case a cat might have clawed at his tail and damaged it."

"Poor gerbil," Mandy sighed. "What happens next, Mom?"

"Well, first, I'll put him into a cage and allow him to calm down for a while," Dr. Emily replied.

"Will you be able to make his tail better, Dr. Emily?" asked James.

Dr. Emily looked from one worried face to the other. "I'm afraid I'll have to remove most of it," she said gently. "The skin won't grow back. If we leave it like that, the sore part will become infected and make him ill."

Mandy blinked hard and James took off his glasses and wiped them on his T-shirt.

"He should be all right afterward," Dr. Emily continued. "He just won't be able to balance so well when he's sitting up or jumping."

"But you really think he'll be okay, Mom?"

"I'll need to take a closer look at him, Mandy. But from what I have seen he appears to be healthy enough. His coat is sleek and in good condition and there aren't any sore spots around his eyes, ears, or nose. Either he hasn't been living wild for long, or he's managed to find the right sort of food to keep him healthy."

"His coat is sleek, isn't it?" said Mandy, looking a bit happier.

"And his eyes are very bright," said James. "But that might be because he's still frightened."

Dr. Emily nodded and explained that gerbils were often nervous when being handled by someone they didn't know.

"Or," Mandy said thoughtfully, "if he's been living wild for a while, he could have forgotten about a human being a friend."

"Yes, that's possible," Dr. Emily agreed. "Now," she added, picking up the carrier, "I'll go and find him a cage and leave him in the unit for a while."

Mandy and James went back into the kitchen where Mandy told her dad all about the gerbil.

"I wonder where he escaped from?" said Dr. Adam. "I haven't heard anything about a lost gerbil."

"We need a name for him," said James. "Why don't we take Blackie for a walk later and try to think of one?"

"That's an excellent idea, James," said Dr. Adam, smiling down at Mandy's friend.

Mandy managed a smile, too. She was still worried about the gerbil, but it would be great thinking of a name for him. And it would be fun taking Blackie for a walk. Blackie was James's Labrador puppy. He hadn't learned to do as he was told yet, but Mandy really loved Blackie.

"I'll come by right after lunch," said Mandy. "And we could drop in at Lilac Cottage afterwards and tell Grandma and Grandpa about the gerbil."

"Lunch!" gasped James in dismay. "I'm going to be really late. I'd better get going."

Mandy watched James run off and then went into the kitchen to get ready for lunch. She kept glancing toward the door, though, impatient for her mom to tell her more about the gerbil.

4

Name Problem

"He's probably about five or six months old," said Dr. Emily when she came into the kitchen. "I picked him up to put him in the cage and his weight is fine. Apart from his tail, there doesn't seem to be anything wrong with him."

"It's too bad about his tail," Mandy sighed. "I hope he knows you'll only be doing it to help him."

Dr. Emily gave her a quick hug. "I had a little chat with him and explained what I was going to do and why I had to do it," she replied. "He squeaked at me and I think he was telling me 'Okay.'"

Mandy giggled. Her mom knew just how to cheer her up.

While she was eating her lunch, Mandy's mind buzzed with possible names for the gerbil. Sandy . . . Goldie . . . Woffles . . . No! That sounded like a name for a rabbit. Jimmy . . . Lucky . . . Squeaker . . .

Mandy shook her head. None of them sounded right. She'd have to wait and see if James had any better ideas.

When Mandy got close to James's house she could see Blackie's nose poking out through the bars in the front gate. She laughed out loud and Blackie gave a joyful woof. Then he leaped up at the gate, scrabbling his front paws crazily along the top of it.

"He's been watching for you," said James, running to get hold of Blackie's collar. "I told him we'd be going for a walk when you got here. I'm sure he understood."

"Of course he did," said Mandy, opening the gate and slipping through. "He's a smart boy; aren't you, Blackie?"

Blackie's tail wagged furiously and he lowered his head to Mandy's feet. "No, Blackie," Mandy chuckled. "There aren't any laces for you to pull at!"

The Labrador loved pulling at shoelaces, but this afternoon Mandy was wearing flip-flops. Blackie soon found something else to do. He started sniffing and licking at Mandy's bare toes. "Ooh!" she laughed. "That tickles. Stop it, Blackie!"

James pulled Blackie away and clipped his leash on. "Now calm down and walk nicely," he said sternly, opening the gate.

As they walked toward the park, Mandy told her friend what her mom had said. Then she sighed and added, "I guess she'll be operating on his tail tomorrow, after he's settled."

"It's too bad about his tail," said James. "But it's lucky we found him before it got any worse."

"Lucky is one of the names I thought of while I was eating my lunch," said Mandy.

James wrinkled his nose and shook his head. He didn't think Lucky sounded right, either. They walked on in silence for a while, both trying to think of a good name. By the time they reached the park neither of them had thought of one.

"There's Arnie," said Mandy, "sitting next to the bench by the tennis courts."

"Guarding Mr. Jordan's bag while he plays tennis," said James.

Mike Jordan was about Grandpa Hope's age. He hadn't lived in Welford long, but he got to know people because of Arnie.

Everyone loved Arnie. He was a comical-looking dog who was always getting into places he couldn't get himself out of. He was dark brown, tan, and white — a cross between a dachshund and a Boston terrier. His body was long and he had a very broad, muscular chest. His front legs curved outward slightly and seemed too long for his body. His tail was long and curled over. He had a really cute face and big ears that stood straight up.

"We'll have to tell Arnie how we rescued the gerbil," James joked as they wandered over to him.

Mandy smiled. Arnie was *always* rescuing things. Hedgehogs, baby birds, kittens — if any small creature was where Arnie thought it shouldn't be, he'd pick it up gently in his mouth and take it home. Then, Mr. Jordan would have to try to find out where the animal had come from.

"Arnie's name really fits him," Mandy said as she bent down to stroke him. "I wish we could think of a good name for our gerbil."

"*Our* gerbil?" asked James, smiling as Blackie and Arnie greeted each other.

"Well, he's ours for the time being," said Mandy, waving to Mr. Jordan as he came to pick up a tennis ball from the back of the court.

Mandy knew that if nobody claimed the gerbil they'd have to find him a good home. The Hopes were too busy looking after other people's animals for them to have a pet of their own.

"I'm going to ask Mom and Dad if we can take care of him," said Mandy. "It would be great, because gerbils are awake in the day. I want to do *everything* for him: feed him, clean his cage, play with him . . ." She paused and bit her lip. "He'll have to get used to us before we can play with him. We'll have to talk to him a lot, then he'll come to us when we call him."

"Yup." James frowned. "So he really does need a name. Let's start walking again, Mandy. I can think better then."

They said good-bye to Arnie. He didn't seem to mind them going, and he soon went back to guarding his master's bag.

Mandy noticed a small crowd standing and sitting around the bandstand. "There must be a brass band concert today," she said.

James nodded. "The local band plays here most Sundays. We can hear it from our garden."

"I wonder if Pam Stanton's here," said Mandy. "Her dad plays the trombone."

Pam was in Mandy's class at school. She had a guinea pig named Ginny, and Mandy and James knew she'd want to hear about the gerbil.

"She is," James pointed. "See, Mandy, she's over there."

"So are Grandma and Grandpa!" said Mandy, starting to run.

"Hi," said Pam, when they ran up to her. "Did you get to see the harvest mouse? Your grandpa's just been telling me you heard one inside a mouse house." She bent down to stroke Blackie.

Mandy and James told Pam, Grandma, and Grandpa about the gerbil.

"Good heavens," said Grandma, shaking her head. "Who would have thought it? That's one very bright gerbil."

"It's fantastic!" said Pam. "I wish I'd been there. You'll have to pin a notice on the school bulletin board tomorrow telling everyone you've found a gerbil. Just think," she continued, "if it hadn't been for our harvest mouse survey — "

"That's it!" James interrupted. "Mandy, I've just thought of a perfect name for him."

5

Harvey

"Harvey!" James said, beaming triumphantly. "Because we found him in a harvest mouse's house!"

"Harvey," repeated Mandy. "Yes! It's absolutely perfect!"

Pam looked at them and burst out laughing.

"What's wrong? Don't you like it, Pam?" asked Mandy, feeling disappointed.

"It's not that! It's just that . . ." Pam laughed again, ". . . whenever my dad sees Ginny he wiggles his nose at her and my mom says he looks more like a *gerbil* than a guinea pig," she chortled, glancing toward the bandstand where the band members were busy setting everything up. "And Dad's name is Harvey!"

Mandy and James looked toward Mr. Stanton. He was holding his trombone to his mouth and Mandy giggled. "Wouldn't our Harvey look funny playing a trombone?" she said.

Grandma laughed, too, then she held a finger to her mouth; the concert was about to begin.

The music was soft and slow at first, but gradually it got louder and faster. Blackie sat down. His ears pricked up. He held his head first to one side, then to the other, then . . . he pointed his head to the sky and started howling!

"Oh, no!" said James, frantically tugging at

Blackie's collar. "Let's get away from here, Mandy!" But Blackie didn't want to move. James's face grew redder and redder as he tried to get Blackie to stand up.

In the end, Grandpa bent down and lifted Blackie's bottom from the ground. Then he dug in his pocket and passed a couple of bills to Mandy. "Go and buy some ice cream," he said, his mouth close to Blackie's ears.

Ice cream! Blackie seemed to recognize that. He looked up at James and then tugged at his leash.

"Thanks, Mr. Hope," James called over his shoulder as he and Mandy hurried off with Blackie leading the way.

Mandy bought two ice creams from the truck. Blackie started to whine when he saw them and looked pleadingly at James. "You don't deserve any," James told him. "But . . ." James pulled a doggy treat out of his pocket and put the *tiniest* bit of ice cream on it. "Just to let him think he's got one of his own," he said to Mandy.

Mandy nodded. They knew dogs shouldn't have ice cream, but the speck James had given him wouldn't do any harm.

"Let's go back to Animal Ark," said Mandy when they'd finished eating. "I can't wait to ask Mom and Dad if we can look after Harvey."

Dr. Emily was sitting at the big pine table doing some paperwork when Mandy, James, and Blackie burst into the kitchen.

"We've thought of a perfect name for the gerbil, Mom!" said Mandy.

Mandy's mom agreed that Harvey was a good name, then she looked closely at Mandy's face. "I recognize that expression, Mandy Hope," she said. "What else have you thought of?"

Mandy rubbed one foot against the ankle of her other foot. "I know we won't be able to *keep* Harvey, Mom, but please could James and I look after him while he is here?"

"We mean clean out his cage and everything, Dr. Emily," said James, shoving his glasses back on to the bridge of his nose.

Mandy said they knew it would mean a lot of hard work and they'd have to be very patient with Harvey. "He'll be frightened of us for a while, so we'll have to talk to him a lot so he gets to know us and trust us. And I know we'd have to *learn* exactly how to look after him, Mom. But we'd read about that, wouldn't we, James?"

Dr. Adam's deep laugh sounded from the doorway. He had a couple of slim books and some pamphlets in one hand. He held them up and waved them at Mandy and James. Blackie woofed and darted over to say hello. He was very fond of Mandy's dad.

"Whoa there, young fella! These aren't for you," said Dr. Adam as Blackie leaped up, trying to reach the books. "They're for Mandy and James."

"For us, Dad?" Mandy hurried to take them from him.

"From the clinic," he told her.

Mandy glanced down at them, then she flung her arms around her dad's waist. "How did you know?" she said. "How did you know what we were talking about?"

"Magic," he teased, ruffling her hair. Blackie gave another woof and jumped up again.

"Both of you at once is too much!" Dr. Adam protested.

Mandy moved away and thrust the books and pamphlets into her friend's hands with a huge smile. They were all about caring for gerbils; feeding them, taming them, keeping them healthy . . .

"Wow!" said James, grinning back at Mandy.

Dr. Emily smiled. "We guessed you would ask if you could look after him," she said. "But," she added, "you'll have to wait until he starts recovering."

"That'll give us time to read the books and pamphlets, right, James?"

"From cover to cover," he said.

"I put a notice on the clinic bulletin board asking if anyone has lost a gerbil," said Dr. Adam.

"And we'll put one on the school bulletin board," said James.

"That's a good idea," Dr. Adam said. "But if nobody's claimed him in a week or so . . ." he looked meaningfully at Mandy, ". . . we'll have to start looking for a good home for him."

Mandy met his gaze and nodded. She didn't like thinking about that, but at least they'd have Harvey for a little while.

James had wandered to the kitchen table and was sitting with his head propped in his hands — he was reading one of the pamphlets already. Mandy dragged a chair around so she

could sit next to him. She reached out for one of the books and opened it.

A few seconds later her mom said, "I thought I'd have the kitchen to myself for a while to do my paperwork, and now there are two eager beavers at the table and one pest of a dog chewing at my laces!"

James jumped up looking really worried. Mandy giggled and pulled him back down. She knew her mom was teasing. "We want to make sure we know everything there is to know, Mom. While Harvey's here, he'll be the best-looked-after gerbil ever!" she said.

6

Spreading the News

Next morning there was no sign of James when Mandy arrived at the huge, old oak tree on the village green. They always met there to bike the rest of the way to school together.

Mandy propped her bike against the tree and went over to the pond to look at the tadpoles. She knelt down and peered into the water.

The tadpoles were getting really big now; some of them had grown two tiny back legs. Mandy knew their front legs were growing as well, but they were hidden by little gill plates. When the gills disappeared she'd be able to see the front legs, too. And, soon after, the tadpoles' tails would get shorter and shorter . . .

"Then," Mandy murmured, "you'll change into little frogs and be hopping all over the green!"

Mandy watched for a little while longer until she heard someone calling her name. She stood up and turned to see Paul Stevens propping his bike next to hers. Paul was eight and a year younger. He was in the same class as James. He lived in Jasmine Cottage near Grandma and Grandpa.

"Hi, Paul," said Mandy, walking to meet him. "How's Paddy?" Paddy was Paul's Exmoor pony.

"Fantastic," beamed Paul. "We went for a great ride over the moors with the pony club yesterday. How's the gerbil? Your grandpa told me about him last night. Did you really find him in one of our mouse houses?"

Mandy nodded, then told Paul the whole story. "I couldn't see him this morning. He's having his operation at nine o'clock and Mom didn't want him disturbed before."

"He'll probably be wide awake and running around when you get home from school," said Paul.

"I hope so," said Mandy. "Then tomorrow or the next day, James and I can start looking after him," she finished off happily.

"Let me know if you want any help," said Paul. "You and James were a big help when I first got Paddy from the rescue shelter."

Mandy explained that because Harvey had been living wild he'd probably be nervous around humans for a while.

Paul nodded. "Do you think I could come and see him when he isn't frightened of people anymore?"

"Of course you can, Paul," replied Mandy.

The church clock chimed in the distance and Mandy sighed. "I don't know where James is, but we'd better go or we'll be late."

Welford Village School was on Church Street — a small road off Main Street at the side of the church.

James caught up with Paul and Mandy just as they were biking past the church. He was pedaling furiously and looked hot and out of breath.

"Mom says Harvey's doing fine," Mandy told him. "Why are you so late, James? Did you oversleep?"

"I forgot the mouse count notebook," he replied breathlessly. "I had to go back for it."

The notebook was important. They were supposed to take it to Mrs. Garvie, the principal, before the school assembly. Mrs. Garvie was going to tell the whole school the results of the first mouse counting day.

"I almost forgot the notice for the bulletin board," Mandy admitted as they rode toward the bike rack. She and James had written it yesterday before James had gone home.

When they'd wheeled their bikes into the special racks, Mandy opened her schoolbag and pulled the notice out to show Paul. It had a drawing of a mouse house in the middle, and around the drawing were the words:

Mandy Hope and James Hunter found a gerbil in a mouse house.

We are calling him Harvey.

If anyone has lost a gerbil please contact Animal Ark.

"What will happen if you don't find his owner?" Paul asked. "He probably doesn't belong to anyone from school because someone would have put a notice on the board about a lost gerbil."

Mandy told him her dad put a notice up on Animal Ark's board, too.

"But if nobody claims him, we'll have to find him a good home," said James. Then he looked up at the school building and saw Mrs. Garvie looking down at them from her office window. "We'd better hurry, Mandy. I think Mrs. Garvie is waiting for the notebook."

Paul said he'd put the notice up for them.

"Put it in the best place you can," Mandy called as she and James ran off.

"I see you found twenty-eight mouse houses with the food gone?" Mrs. Garvie said a short while later, as she looked at the mouse counting notebook.

Mandy and James nodded.

"And we decided to count one harvest mouse for every three empty mouse houses. So, how many harvest mice can we say are living in or around the reed beds?"

"At least nine, Mrs. Garvie," said Mandy.

The principal nodded and smiled. "I'll give out these details right after assembly. Then I'll send a report to all the other schools taking part in the survey. And I should be hearing from them soon with details of their first mouse counts."

Mandy and James looked at each other. Should they tell Mrs. Garvie about Harvey? She might not see the bulletin board until *after* she'd sent her report to all the other schools and they might be interested to know what they'd found in one of the mouse houses.

"Is there something else?" Mrs. Garvie asked.

Then Mandy and James told her all about it — from when Grandpa had heard something inside the mouse house, right up to why they'd decided to call the gerbil Harvey.

"Goodness," said Mrs. Garvie. "I think I'll have to make a special announcement about this after the mouse count report. Or better still, how about you two coming up on the platform and telling everyone yourselves?"

"We made a notice for the bulletin board and Paul Stevens is putting it up for us right now," James said in alarm. He didn't like the idea of standing up in front of the whole school!

"But we didn't tell the whole story," said Mandy. "I'll do the talking, James, if you want."

Mandy crossed her fingers while she waited for James's reply. She didn't *really* want to go up onto the platform on her own.

"No . . . it's okay, I'll do it with you," James said.

Mandy smiled happily at Mrs. Garvie. She knew James wouldn't let her down.

When the time came during assembly for Mandy and James to go up onto the platform, James felt nervous all over again. But once Mandy had started talking, he joined in eagerly. He even asked if anyone had lost a gerbil.

But nobody had lost a gerbil and everybody wondered where Harvey had lived before he found his way into one of their mouse houses.

Then Pam Stanton waved her hand in the air. She asked Mrs. Garvie if the school could have a Harvey announcement every day. "He *was* found in one of *our* mouse houses," she pointed out.

Mrs. Garvie thought every day would be a bit too much, but she said James and Mandy could give the school an update once a week.

"And," said Mandy to James at the end of the assembly, "we should have plenty to tell everyone next week. By then we'll have spent four or five days looking after Harvey. Oh," she added, hugging herself with excitement, "I just can't wait for Mom to tell us we can start!"

7

Making Friends

After school, James and Mandy rode quickly to
Animal Ark. Maybe they'd be able to see Harvey for a few minutes!

"That's if he's all right," said Mandy. She'd
been worrying all day.

"I'm sure he will be," said James.

"I wonder if he'll be able to eat yet?" said

Mandy as they wheeled their bikes up the garden path. "If we knew his favorite food, we could put some in his cage to show him we're friends."

"What treats do Terry and Gerry like best?" James asked. Terry and Gerry were Mandy's class gerbils. Mandy and the rest of her class all helped look after them.

"Terry likes raisins and Gerry *loves* tomato," Mandy replied.

"Well, Harvey might like both of those," said James. "Let's ask your mom if it would be all right to give him some of each."

"Good idea," said Mandy. "Let's go and find her."

Dr. Emily was walking out of the unit when Mandy and James hurried into the clinic. "Harvey's fine," she said before Mandy had time to ask.

Mandy ran to hug her. "I knew he *would* be okay, Mom," she said. "But I couldn't help worrying."

"You can have five minutes with him," said

Dr. Emily. Her green eyes twinkled when she saw their excited faces.

Then Mandy's words tumbled out quickly as she told her mom what she and James had thought of. ". . . So do you think it would be all right to give Harvey a couple of raisins and a small piece of tomato?"

"I think it's a very good idea," said Dr. Emily. "But remember to move your hands very slowly when you're putting anything in the cage."

"So we don't frighten him," said James.

"That's right," said Dr. Emily. "And it's a little too soon to try to get him to take anything from your fingers. I think you'd better just put his treats near his food dish."

"I hope Harvey will like them," said Mandy.

"Me, too." Her mom smiled. "It might stop him from chewing the wood chips off the floor of his cage and throwing bits out through the bars!"

"Is that what he's been doing?" Mandy asked.

Dr. Emily nodded. "I think Harvey might be feeling a little bored. I've put a couple of cardboard tubes in his cage, but I think he needs something more interesting to play with," she told them. "I'm sure I can leave that to you two, though."

"You bet!" said James, edging to one side and trying to peer into the unit.

"Go ahead," Dr. Emily laughed. "You can look at Harvey while I get his treats."

Mandy followed James into the unit and over to Harvey's cage. There was no sign of the gerbil. Mandy thought he must be in his wooden nesting box at the back of the cage, but suddenly James pointed to one of the cardboard tubes.

The lower half of Harvey's face was peeping out of one end. His whiskers were twitching and he was staring at them, his eyes round and dark and curious.

"Let's crouch down and put our faces close to the cage," Mandy suggested quietly.

James nodded and, moving together, they slowly and silently bent down.

A little scratchy sound came from the tube — Harvey's claws moving inside. For a moment it seemed as though he was going to wriggle backward and hide away. Mandy and James froze, hardly daring to breathe. But Harvey stayed where he was.

"I think it would be all right for us to talk around him," Mandy whispered. "Get him used to the sound of our voices." Just then Harvey's front feet crept a little way out of the tube. The rest of his face began to appear and Mandy smiled as his ears, which must have been flattened against the inside of the tube, suddenly popped up.

"Hello, Harvey," Mandy said softly. "We won't hurt you. We want to be your friends."

James told Harvey he was a very brave gerbil.

Harvey stared solemnly back. Mandy was sure he was waiting for one of them to speak again.

Just then the unit door opened. Harvey scrabbled his feet, gave a frightened squeak, and, quick as a flash, withdrew his head and moved right back inside the tube.

Mandy and James stood up, and Simon, who'd recently come to work at Animal Ark, walked toward them. He was holding a plate containing a piece of tomato and two raisins. Simon wasn't a vet, he was a nurse. He helped with operations and looked after animals who had to stay for a while. He kept the animals clean and comfortable, soothed them and talked to them, changed dressings, fed them, and gave them any medicine they needed.

Mandy and James liked Simon. He was always willing to answer their questions and he knew a lot about animals.

"Your mom's been called out," Simon told Mandy. "She asked me to bring this in for you to give to the gerbil. And she said to remind you not to stay in here too long."

"We'll put Harvey's treats in the cage, then watch for a very *little* while to see if he comes out," said Mandy. "Will you wait with us, Si-mon?"

"Sure," he said. "But that doesn't mean you spend any more time with Harvey!"

Mandy smiled, then passed James the piece of tomato. He put it carefully into the cage. Mandy put the raisins next to it.

The three of them stepped back and waited. But not even a whisker appeared from the tube. "Come on," said Simon. "He'll probably pop out and gobble everything up as soon as we've gone."

"He let us look at him and talk to him for a while, Simon," Mandy said as she closed the unit door behind them. "But he didn't come out of the tube all the way, so we couldn't see his tail end."

"He's still got a bit of a tail," Simon told her. "About this much," he added, holding his thumb and forefinger about an inch apart.

"Maybe he'll let us see *all* of him next time," said James.

Simon nodded. "Gerbils are curious and

nosy little creatures," he said. "In time, wanting to know and see what's going on makes them forget their fear."

"Dr. Emily said he needs something interesting to play with," said James. "If we could think of something to put in his cage tomorrow, do you think he'd feel curious enough to go and look at it?"

Simon thought it was a good idea. Now all Mandy and James needed to do was to figure out something really interesting and exciting to make for Harvey.

"Call your mom and ask if you can stay for dinner, James," Mandy suggested. She knew her parents wouldn't mind; James was always welcome at Animal Ark.

"Okay," James agreed. "Then we can really think about it."

"Remember how we made an adventure playground for Frisky?" said James as he and Mandy set the table. "Well, maybe we could do something like that for Harvey."

Frisky was a small Russian hamster who had stayed with Mandy's grandparents while his owner was on vacation. Mandy and James had helped look after him for the whole week and they'd made his cage a really exciting play place for him.

"I read in one of those books Dad gave us that gerbils tend to be even more adventurous than hamsters," said Mandy. "We'll have to think of all sorts of things he can wiggle into and climb up. Maybe we could make him a maze out of little cardboard boxes with holes in the tops."

"We could leave one or two boxes open and put a little ladder or a thick branch in so he'll be able to climb up and down and in and out of them," said James.

"Sounds like gerbil talk to me," said a voice from the doorway.

It was Dr. Adam. He came in and put a narrow box with rounded ends on the table. "Nuts and raisins for you," he told Mandy. "Mrs. Edwards sent them. I was just there to check Tilly's puppies."

Mrs. Edwards had a grocery shop and Tilly was her corgi.

"How many puppies did she have, Dad? Are they okay?"

Dr. Adam smiled. "She had two; Mom and pups are doing fine. The puppies are both boys and they look just like their dad."

"Isn't their dad a corgi, too?" Mandy asked.

"No!" Dr. Adam's eyes twinkled. "Their dad is Mike Jordan's Arnie."

Mandy laughed. "We'd better not tell Arnie about his sons. He'll want to take them home and put them in his basket."

James didn't say a word. Mandy wondered why and turned to look at him. James was staring hard at the box of nuts and raisins. "You can have some if you want," Mandy told him.

Her friend shook his head. "It's not them, it's the box they're in," he explained. "I've thought of just the right thing to make for Harvey."

8

Gerbil Jinks

Mandy was so curious about James's idea she couldn't eat her dinner fast enough. She finished long before her friend did and then had to wait for him!

She kept looking at the box, but she just couldn't guess what James had in mind.

But James finished at last and Mandy jumped

up to clear the table. Then she took the lid off the box and tipped the nuts and raisins into a small bowl. James reached for a nut and nibbled it as he gazed thoughtfully at the box.

"We need a small square or oblong box that will fit inside this one at one end," he said. "And some smaller boxes, too . . . and the inside of a paper towel roll to cut down for a funnel and —"

"I get it!" Mandy interrupted excitedly. "We're going to turn the box into a boat!"

"Yes!" James grinned up at her. "A cargo boat!"

"And the cargo will be food," said Mandy. "We've got some of the cargo already. We can hide some of the raisins or pieces of carrot or turnip or a grape inside the little boxes. Oh, it's a great idea, James! I'm sure there are cardboard tubes and little boxes in the clinic."

The cargo boat soon took shape. James carefully cut two holes in the box they were using for the bridge area, one hole for a door and the other to push the funnel into. Mandy cut holes in the smaller boxes and arranged them at the other end of the boat in a sort of maze.

"If Harvey likes his cargo boat, we can keep adding things to it," Mandy said happily.

"Mmm," James nodded. "A ladder would be good, wouldn't it? We could stand the boat on a block of wood or another box, so he'd have to climb up the ladder to get on to it."

Mandy decided a box would be better than a block of wood. "Because then," she said, "we can make *another* play area inside the box, and it will be —"

"A multistory play area!" James finished the sentence for her. "Wow!" he added. "I can't wait for tomorrow."

At school next day, Mrs. Garvie read the reports from some of the other schools taking part in the harvest mouse survey. One school said that none of the food had gone from the tennis ball mouse houses, and two other schools reported quite a high success rate.

"But nobody else found a gerbil in a mouse house!" said Carrie Anderson, who was in Mandy's class. "I've got something for Harvey," she said, and she handed Mandy a small wooden ball. "I bought it for Bingo, my bird," Carrie told her. "He doesn't play with it, so I thought Harvey might like it."

"That's great, Carrie. Thanks," said Mandy.

When Mandy went to find James at play-time, he showed her a wooden brick with two holes in it.

"I brought it for Harvey," said Amy Fenton. "It's one especially for pets. Someone bought it for Minnie, but she's already got lots of play-things." Minnie was Amy's white mouse.

Mandy smiled. "Tell Minnie thank you," she said, then she showed James and Amy the little wooden ball Carrie had given her.

It wasn't Mandy's turn to feed Terry and Gerry, the class gerbils, but she watched Richard Tanner and Jill Redfern while they did it. She wanted to see what the gerbils liked best after raisins and tomato.

"I always bring Terry a small piece of parsley when it's my turn to feed him," said Jill.

"And Gerry likes sunflower seeds," said Richard, laughing as the gerbil scurried over and climbed into his hand to nibble the seed.

Mandy couldn't wait for the day when Harvey would be tame enough to do that!

"I know we've got to be patient," she said to James as they rode home from school. "But it'll be so nice when Harvey starts to trust us!"

When they hurried into the clinic, Dr. Adam greeted them with a smile. "I'm sure Harvey is waiting for you," he said. "He's had his nose pressed to the cage bars for the last ten minutes."

"Does he look all right?" Mandy asked. She felt a little bit worried about seeing him with just a tiny tail.

"He looks great," Dr. Adam assured her.

As soon as they went into the unit, Harvey started squeaking. Mandy beamed at James and they walked slowly toward the cage, talking in low voices.

They got closer and closer to the cage. Harvey squeaked again and then he rose up on his hind legs and gripped the cage bars with his front claws.

"This is a nice welcome," said Mandy, crouching down slowly. "And Dad's right. He looks great, James. His tiny tail doesn't make him look strange at all."

"He's got such a cute face, you don't really notice his tail's shorter than it should be," said James.

Harvey hadn't moved away from the cage bars, so James crouched down, too. "Hello, Harvey," he said. "We've made you something to play with. We'll go and get it in a minute. We'll bring you some treats to nibble, too. Then we'll feed you and give you some fresh water."

Harvey moved his head to one side and stared at James.

"I think he's starting to like us talking to him," Mandy said, and Harvey turned his head slightly and looked at her.

Then, very, very slowly, Mandy walked her fingers up the cage bars until they were close to Harvey's front paws. The gerbil pulled his body back a little way when she ran the tip of one finger over his curled claws, but he didn't take his paw away.

"See if he'll let you stroke his tummy, Mandy," said James.

"Okay," breathed Mandy, slowly moving her fingers down the bars.

Mandy stroked the soft, pale gold fur four times before Harvey decided he'd been brave enough! He moved away quickly with a little squeak and disappeared inside a cardboard tube.

Feeling happy and excited, Mandy and James went to find Dr. Adam to tell him the good news.

"That's really good progress," he said, smiling at them.

Mandy nodded. "And now we're going to get his cargo boat and some little treats to hide in the boxes. Do you think it would be all right to give him some sunflower seeds, Dad?"

"Just one or two," he said, going on to explain that too many sunflower seeds could cause skin problems for a gerbil.

Mandy said they'd hide only one sunflower seed to be on the safe side.

When they went into the kitchen, Dr. Emily was preparing dinner. "It's salad," she said. "I'm making it now so it will be ready to eat as soon as the clinic hours are over."

Mandy and James then told her all about Harvey, too, and they showed her the wooden ball and the brick with holes in it.

"That was nice of Carrie and Amy," said Dr. Emily. "But you'd better wash them in mild disinfectant and let them dry before you give them to Harvey, just to make sure there aren't any germs on them."

"We'll do that after we've given him this," said Mandy, reaching for the cargo boat she'd tucked away in a safe corner. "He can have them tomorrow."

James was watching Dr. Emily grate some cheese. She smiled and handed him a piece.

"Gerbils like cheese, don't they?" Mandy said. "I read it in one of the pamphlets."

"Yes, you can cut a small piece for him," her mom said.

"So we'll hide cheese, a sunflower seed, and . . . and what else, James?"

"Carrot?" said James, pointing to the bowl of salad.

"There'll be nothing left for us to eat at this rate," Dr. Emily teased as she lifted a small teaspoonful of grated carrot from the bowl.

When they'd hidden the food in three of the boxes in the little maze, they hurried through to the clinic and into the unit.

James opened Harvey's cage and carefully slid the cargo boat in. "Look, Mandy, he's watching from inside the tube," he said.

And almost before James had closed the cage door, Harvey was scampering eagerly toward his new boat. He ran all around the outside of it, sniffing and squeaking to himself. Then he climbed inside and went through the round door of the box that had the paper-towel-roll funnel sticking up through its top.

They could hear him moving around, then Mandy gave a little gasp and pointed to the funnel. It was slowly rising upward.

"He must be pushing the end that's inside the box with his head!" said James. "Isn't he smart? He's making up a game of his own!"

Harvey pushed the paper towel roll all the way out and the next minute he popped up through the hole where it had been. He sat on the top of the box for a couple of seconds, his nose and whiskers twitching.

"It looks as if he can still balance all right," said James.

"He's wobbling a little," said Mandy, "but not much!" Then she smiled as Harvey jumped down and ran to the other end of the boat to the maze she'd made with the small boxes.

He's going to the one where I've hidden the cheese! thought Mandy, watching with big, round eyes.

Harvey carried the little square of cheese out, jumped over the side of the boat, and put the cheese down in the middle of his cage. Then he climbed back onto the boat and into the maze. This time he made straight for the box with the sunflower seed.

Mandy and James listened carefully and then grinned at each other. They could hear the gerbil munching on it.

"I wonder if he'll find the carrot next," said Mandy.

Harvey went into the box with the carrot, but he came out quickly, jumped over the side again, and made his way to the piece of cheese. He ate about half of it, then sat on his haunches and rubbed his paws over his face. He was cleaning himself!

He cleaned his eyes, his ears, his nose, and his mouth, then he lowered his front legs to the ground and ran into his nesting box.

"Wow!" said James. "He had a really good time."

"I think he's starting to get quite tame already," said Mandy. "I'm sure he kept checking to see if we were watching when he was playing on his boat."

Mandy gave a small sigh as they went out of the unit. The quicker Harvey became tame, the quicker they'd have to try to find a home for him!

Mr. Jordan was in the waiting room with Arnie, so Mandy and James went to say hello.

"What's wrong with Arnie?" Mandy asked, bending to stroke him.

"He decided he wanted to look after the kitten next door," said Mr. Jordan. "He ran in through the cat flap, then got stuck!" Mr. Jordan didn't have a cat. But Mandy knew he lived in the house in Meadow Lane where the Greenes used to live. They'd probably put the cat flap in the door for their cat.

The cat's name was Tabby and she'd had six kittens just before the Greenes had moved. Mandy had found them all a home at Westmoor House, a retirement home about a mile away.

"I had to give Arnie a good hard tug to get him out," Mr. Jordan explained. "The poor boy yelped quite hard. I think he's only a bit bruised, but we're going on vacation tomorrow, so I'm getting him checked just to be sure."

While Mandy and James petted Arnie, Mr. Jordan asked how the gerbil was. He'd heard all about him from Mandy's grandpa.

"He's so smart!" said James. "You should have seen him playing on the boat we made for him. He's really clever, isn't he, Mandy?"

Mandy nodded and felt a little sad again. "We'll need to find him a home soon," she said, looking hopefully up at Mr. Jordan. It would be great if Harvey could stay in Welford. Then she and James would be able to visit him.

Mr. Jordan shook his head. "I couldn't chance having a gerbil," he said. "Arnie would want to pick him up and carry him around. And *we* know he wouldn't hurt him but . . ."

Mandy nodded. "But Harvey wouldn't know that," she agreed. "He'd be frightened."

"Don't worry, Mandy," said James, as he got ready to go. "Harvey's going to turn into a really fantastic pet. I'm sure we'll be able to find him a good home."

9

A Brilliant Idea

By the time the weekend came, Mandy and James weren't feeling so confident about Harvey. True, he always seemed to be waiting for them when they hurried to see him after school. He looked at them when they talked to him and he let them stroke him through the cage bars. But he still ran and hid in a tube or in his nesting box whenever they put anything in the cage or when they gave him fresh food and water.

And although he played all sorts of games in, on, and around the boxes on the cargo boat, he didn't pay attention to the wooden ball or the brick. Grandpa had brought a tiny terra-cotta plant pot, but Harvey ignored that, too.

On Saturday morning, Harvey wouldn't even come to the front of the cage when Mandy called him. He poked his head out of his nesting box, but that was all.

"I don't think he's sick," she said to James. "He's eaten quite a lot of the food we gave him yesterday afternoon and his eyes are nice and bright."

"He just seems to have gone back to being nervous," sighed James. "Let's go away for a little while. He might be all right when we come back."

When they went back a couple of hours later, Harvey was standing up at the cage bars.

But he ran off when Mandy tried to stroke his tummy.

Mandy and James mentioned the problem to Simon, and he suggested Mandy make a play area for Harvey.

"Your hands might not seem so big and threatening inside a larger space," he said. "And he might play with more things if he had more room to play in. There are quite a few tall cardboard boxes waiting to be collected for recycling. You could use them as a barrier."

"We could put his cage inside the area and leave the door open," said Mandy. "And if Harvey comes out, we can take his cage away and clean it out. It's a great idea. Thanks, Simon!"

Dr. Emily said they could make a play area in the kitchen as long as they protected the floor with cardboard and paper. "And," she advised, "when you take his cage away, take the nesting box out of it and put it in the play area. Then Harvey will know he's got somewhere safe to run to."

While Mandy was getting the tall cardboard boxes, James went to get something from the saddlebag on his bike.

"Apple tree twigs and cotton string," he said to Mandy. "I thought we could try making a ladder."

Twenty minutes later, Harvey emerged cautiously through his cage door. He wiggled his nose and twitched his whiskers, then scurried toward the cargo boat. Mandy had put it on top of another box and James had put the twig ladder at the end where the maze was. On top of one of the tiny boxes was a special piece of gerbil chocolate.

In no time at all Harvey climbed up the ladder. Squeaking excitedly, he sniffed at the chocolate drop before eating it. Then he sat up on his haunches as if to say, "What's next?"

Mandy leaned over very slowly, lifted the cage out, and passed it to her friend. James removed the nesting box and carefully put it in the palms of his hands. Then he lowered it carefully into one corner of Harvey's play area.

"Keep your hands under it, James," said Mandy. "Harvey's watching, aren't you, boy?"

Harvey popped into the nesting box and then popped out again — scampering over James's fingers both times.

Mandy tiptoed to the kitchen table and got another piece of chocolate. Then she stuck it between two of James's fingertips. She didn't have time to move away before Harvey darted over to nibble at the chocolate treat. And when he'd finished it, he sniffed at Mandy's hand.

"I haven't got any," she told him. "How about a little stroke instead?"

Harvey didn't move, so Mandy stroked him under the chin with one finger. He stared solemnly up at her as she stroked him, talking softly all the time.

After a while, Harvey squeaked and moved away.

"He's sniffing at the wooden ball," said James. "He's . . . Oh, wow, Mandy!"

They stared in delight as Harvey pushed the ball with his nose, ran after it, and pushed it again. "He's playing soccer," said Mandy.

James leaned over one of the tall boxes and held his hands in a butterfly shape. "Nose the ball to me, Harvey," he said.

Harvey blinked. Then he nosed the ball hard and sent it straight into James's hands. "Goal!" breathed James.

"That was just luck," said Mandy. "He couldn't really have understood."

But James carefully rolled the ball back to the gerbil. "To me, Harvey," he said. And Harvey nosed it back.

"He's a genius!" said Mandy after Harvey had "scored" five goals. "A *gerbil genius*!"

She picked up the ball, made a cup shape with her hand, and rested it on the floor. Harvey scampered over and hopped into her hand. Mandy held her breath and wondered if she

dared to try putting her other hand over the top of Harvey's body.

"Go on," said James when she glanced at him.

"It's okay, Harvey," she murmured. "I won't squash you. What a brave boy." *She was holding Harvey. She was holding him at last!*

After a few seconds, Mandy raised her hands carefully, keeping them close to her body with Harvey facing toward her. And he didn't seem to mind at all!

"I think he likes it!" said James. He'd moved to stand as close as he could. "Look, he's put his face out. He's sniffing at your T-shirt."

Mandy lowered her face and rubbed her nose against Harvey's. And when Harvey looked at her with his big, dark, chocolate-brown eyes, Mandy felt happy and sad at the same time. Harvey was beginning to trust them at last. But now, they'd really have to start trying to find a home for him!

On Monday morning Mandy and James talked to some of their friends about Harvey. They were on their way down to the reed beds to do another mouse count.

There wouldn't be many more mouse counts after this. They knew now that there were harvest mice living near the reeds in Welford — and the reports from the other schools taking part in the survey showed which other areas were home to them as well.

"And even if Welford hasn't got the *most* harvest mice, our results will be the most unusual, because we found Harvey in one of our mouse houses!" said Mandy.

She and James had given a "Harvey update" after assembly, so everyone knew the gerbil was doing well. Since nobody had claimed him, he was now nearly ready to go to a new home.

"Gerbils are happier when they've got another gerbil to play with," said Mandy. "Like Terry and Gerry. But it says in one of my books that they should be introduced to each other before they're eight weeks old or they'll fight. My mom thinks Harvey's five or six months old."

"That means finding somewhere special for Harvey," James said. "He'll need a home where there's someone to play soccer with him and teach him more games. He's *so* smart, he loves learning things!"

When they reached the mouse houses, to Mandy's surprise, James didn't seem to be very interested in what they were doing.

"Are you all right?" she asked after a while.

James nodded. "Just thinking," he said. Then suddenly he stopped dead. "Listen!" he said.

"I've got a brilliant idea! I don't know *how* we didn't think of it before!"

Everyone else stopped whatever they were in the middle of doing with the tennis ball mouse houses and looked at James. They could tell he was excited.

"Wouldn't Mrs. Black's class be the perfect place for Harvey?" said James. "We don't have a class pet."

"Let's ask Mrs. Black about it right now!" said Amy Fenton.

"Yes!" said Paul. "It is a great idea, James!"

"No, don't ask yet!" Mandy said urgently. "When I was in Mrs. Black's class, I asked Mrs. Black if we could have a class pet."

"I remember that," said Pam Stanton. "She said she'd never have another class pet, because the last time she'd allowed her class to have a hamster she'd ended up looking after it herself."

Mandy nodded. "And she could never find anyone to take it home for the school vacations, so she had to do that, too!"

"Well, I couldn't have Harvey for the vacations because of Benji," James admitted gloomily. Benji was James's cat. "Maybe it wasn't such a good idea after all."

"It was, James," said Mandy. "There must be other kids who'd be able to take care of Harvey over the vacations."

"I'm sure I'd be able to," said Paul.

"I would, too," said Amy.

"So, we just need to think up a way of convincing Mrs. Black that there'd always be someone to look after Harvey at school and at home," said Mandy.

"She's coming over," whispered Amy. "Let's talk about it when we get back to school."

10

Making Plans

Today, there were forty mouse houses without any seed left in them. Mrs. Todd and Mrs. Black couldn't understand why their pupils didn't seem more excited — or why they seemed so eager to get back to school!

Mandy and her friends *were* happy to know that even more harvest mice seemed to be using the special feeding houses, but making plans for Harvey to be Mrs. Black's class pet seemed much more important.

During lunch they all went into a little huddle in a corner of the playground.

Pam Stanton said she wished they had a photo of Harvey. "Then we could show it to Mrs. Black. She might think it was a shame that such a beautiful gerbil didn't have a home to go to," she said.

James looked at Paul. "You drew a great picture of Paddy," he said. "Could you come and see Harvey after school and draw a picture of him?"

Paul nodded. "You bet!" he said.

Mandy's eyes sparkled. "We could make the drawing into a card. A card with some rhymes inside . . ."

"Rhymes about a gerbil looking for a home," said Pam.

"A home where there are lots of children, somewhere he could learn things, because he loves learning!" said Amy.

"And we should have a rhyme about how well *we'd* look after him," said James.

"We can leave the card on Mrs. Black's desk with a bunch of flowers!" said Tina Cunningham. "I'm sure Dad will let me pick some out of the garden."

They spent the rest of recess coming up with rhymes. Mandy and James said they would write the card while Paul drew his picture of Harvey.

"And Mrs. Black always goes straight into the classroom when she arrives," said Mandy. "If we all get here a few minutes early tomorrow, we can put the flowers and the card on her desk."

"Then we can peep through the window and watch her face when she reads the card," said James.

Everything went according to plan next morning. Mandy and James had written the Harvey poem on the inside of a piece of folded paper and Paul had drawn Harvey on the outside. It was a really good drawing of Harvey standing up against the bars of his cage. Paul had drawn a speech bubble coming from the gerbil's mouth and inside it he'd written: *Please let me come to school and be your pet!*

Tina Cunningham had brought flowers wrapped in paper, tied with a bow, and Mr. Simpson, the janitor, had allowed James to go into the classroom early and put the card and the flowers on Mrs. Black's desk.

Now they were all looking in at the window, watching Mrs. Black.

"She's smiling," Mandy whispered.

"I bet that's at my line," said James. "It wasn't a very good one."

" '*This gerbil genius will be very happy to be with us . . . if we have him as our class pet. He'll behave very well and listen and learn . . . because that's what classrooms are for!*' " Mandy quoted with a giggle.

"Mine was worse than that!" Pam laughed. " '*Harvey the gerbil is feeling blue. Mrs. Black's got a heart of gold. If she'd allow Harvey to come to school, too, we'd look after him without being told!*' "

Just then, Paul gave a little gasp. Mrs. Black was coming over to the window.

"And what about school vacations?" she asked, popping her head out. "Who'll look after him then?"

Tina, Paul, and Amy dug into their backpacks and each pulled out a letter. "We thought of that, Mrs. Black!" said Amy. "These are from our parents saying we can take Harvey home for vacations."

"We can take turns," said Paul.

"What's he going to live in?" asked Mrs. Black.

They all looked at each other in dismay. They hadn't thought of that.

But then Mandy smiled. "I'm sure Mom and Dad would let us borrow a cage from Animal Ark for a while," she said.

"While we all save up our pocket money to buy him a cage of his own," said Paul. The others nodded.

"Very well," said Mrs. Black. "I'll have a word with Mrs. Garvie during morning break. *If* she agrees, I'll agree to a . . ." she held up a hand as everyone cheered, ". . . to a trial period," she said. "But if Harvey stops you from concentrating on your lessons, or if I think he isn't being well cared for . . ."

"We'll make a list like Mrs. Todd has for looking after Terry and Gerry," said James. "We'll all take turns to do the important things like feeding him and changing his water and cleaning the cage."

"And when you let us choose a reward for finishing our work early, we could choose to play with Harvey," said Tina.

The lining-up bell rang just then. They all sped away and got in line, standing straight and quiet! They were all silently wishing hard for Mrs. Garvie to say yes.

The first part of the morning seemed to go really slowly. And, for once, when recess came, everybody wanted it to end quickly!

Then they wanted it to last longer, because Mrs. Black came into the playground to tell them that Mrs. Garvie had agreed to let them have Harvey for a trial period of two weeks!

11

Harvey on Trial

"You'll never guess what Harvey does now!" Mandy said excitedly to her mom and Simon one day after school.

It was almost two weeks since Dr. Emily had driven Mandy to school with Harvey in the cage that was on loan from Animal Ark. And every day Mandy came home and told her parents and Simon what the gerbil had been up to.

"Well, every time the bell for recess rings, he squeaks and runs up his ladder! Our class was in with Mrs. Black's class today, because we're making a huge map so we can mark off the places where we know harvest mice are living. And we all saw him do it. We think it's because Harvey knows that someone puts his toys in his cage when the bell rings, so he can have recess, too!"

"I expect he'd run up his ladder and squeak if he heard a whistle or some other noise," said Simon.

"Do you think so?" Mandy looked disappointed. "I'll ask Mrs. Black if we can try him with other noises tomorrow," she said.

When Mandy asked next day, Mrs. Black and Mandy's teacher, Mrs. Todd, thought the experiment was a good idea. They decided that the two classes should try it out just before morning recess.

The teachers had opened the dividing doors between the classrooms, because the two classes were working together again on the big map.

A short time before the bell for recess was due to ring, the classes stopped their lesson, and Mrs. Black gave a good, long blow on her playground whistle.

Harvey rose up onto his haunches and stood stock-still. Mrs. Black blew the whistle again — Harvey didn't move. Then Mrs. Todd said that might be because everyone was kneeling on the floor, watching him. "You all start to get up when the bell rings," she pointed out. "I'll make the alarm on my traveling clock buzz and you go to your tables and shuffle papers and push your chairs back."

The alarm clock buzzer sounded and everyone dashed to a table and pretended to be getting ready for break. But still Harvey didn't go to his ladder.

It was only when the real break bell sounded that Harvey dashed to his ladder and ran up it, squeaking louder than ever.

"It seems there's no fooling Harvey," said Mrs. Black, smiling. "He really is a gerbil genius!"

When the others went out to play, Amy Fenton and James stayed behind. Today was one of the days for cleaning out Harvey's cage. On those days, instead of going to the teacher's room, Mrs. Black stayed in the classroom during morning recess with whoever was cleaning out Harvey's cage.

James went to get the big cardboard box with tall sides that they put Harvey into while his cage was being cleaned, and Amy lifted the gerbil out. She was careful to hold him facing her body so he couldn't suddenly jump and land on the floor.

Harvey sat in her hand, twitching his nose as she talked to him. But the second James came and put the box on the floor, he gave a loud squeak.

"He's being clever again," laughed Amy as she lowered Harvey into the box. "He *knows* there are lots of playthings in here."

"He'll start looking for his wooden ball in a minute," said James, as he went to the cage and started to remove the soiled wood chips from the bottom of it.

"I've hidden it under one of the small boxes," he added, glancing across at Mrs. Black. "Harvey will sniff at all the boxes until he finds the right one. Then he'll lift it up with his nose and push it out of the way so he can get the ball."

"That's amazing!" laughed Mrs. Black when Harvey did exactly as James had said he would.

Then she turned as someone knocked on the classroom door. "That should be Mrs. Garvie with my cup of coffee," she said.

"Did you hear that, Harvey?" Amy whispered as Mrs. Black went to open the door. "Mrs. Black said you were amazing! I'm sure she's going to let you stay."

"I heard that, Amy Fenton!" Mrs. Black walked back over with her drink. Amy turned pink and her teacher smiled. "But I must admit you're all taking very good care of him," she said.

"And of his cage," she added, as James went to the sink to scrub Harvey's food dish and water container.

A few minutes later, they heard the lining-up bell. "Gosh!" said James. "I haven't finished Harvey's cage yet." He threw a worried look toward Mrs. Black.

"It's all right, James," she said. "Break started late because of our experiment. I'll give you a few minutes at lunchtime to finish."

"Will he mind going into his cage when

there aren't any wood chips on the floor?" Amy asked anxiously.

"Leave him in his box," said Mrs. Black. "But," she warned as the others came in from the playground, "there'll be big trouble if anyone so much as looks toward the box. I want us to get all the areas marked out on the map this morning."

"I think Mrs. Black might be carrying out a little experiment of her own," James whispered when Mrs. Black was at the far end of the room, handing out colored pens.

Amy nodded. "Seeing if we can behave when we know Harvey isn't in his cage."

It was so interesting finding the areas where all the other schools had carried out their surveys and then drawing tiny pictures of tennis ball mouse houses that nobody looked up from the map at all.

"You're all doing really well," said Mrs. Todd, kneeling down next to Mandy.

"I think we've just about finished," said

Mandy. "We've written the names of the schools as well as drawing mouse houses in the places each school put them. We can't write in how many harvest mice there are in each area until Mrs. Garvie gets the last reports."

"But we can write in how many we think there are in Welford," said James. "We had our last mouse counting day last week."

Mandy gasped and looked at Mrs. Todd. "We haven't marked our school or the reed beds on the map!" she said.

"I wondered when you'd realize that," her teacher smiled.

"So," said Mrs. Black, from where she was kneeling at the other side of the map. "Who's going to be the first to find Welford?"

Everyone knelt closer over the big map. But suddenly, there was a funny little scuffling noise, and James jumped as he felt something brush past his leg and against the inside of his arm.

"Harvey!" he said in astonishment as the gerbil scampered onto the map. "Quick, everyone! Move closer together so he can't escape!"

But Harvey didn't make any attempt to move off the map. Nose down, he ran back and forth and from side to side over it. Then suddenly he stopped. He rose up onto his haunches and stared around at everyone in turn, his brown eyes shining brightly.

"Well," Mrs. Black said softly. "I think that settles it, doesn't it?"

"It's the first time he's disturbed us during a lesson, Mrs. Black," pleaded Amy. "Please give him another chance."

"He must have managed to climb up the side of the box," said James. "If you'll give him another chance, we promise we'll never leave him in it again, unless we're watching him!"

"And — " began Mandy. But she stopped when Mrs. Black held up a hand for silence.

"You can't imagine that I wouldn't let Harvey stay after this!" she said. "Just look at him. Look at *where* he's sitting!"

"Oh!" said James, his eyes huge and round behind his glasses. "He's . . . he's sitting on Welford!" he stuttered.

"That's right," Mrs. Black smiled.

"More than that," said Mrs. Todd. "He's sitting exactly on top of where we want to mark Welford Village School."

Mrs. Black nodded and leaned forward to pick up Harvey. "You're a gerbil genius," she told him. "We couldn't possibly let you go anywhere else now. You've shown us that Welford Village School is where you belong!"

Everyone cheered as Mrs. Black stood up and carried Harvey toward his cage.

"James! Amy!" she said over the cheers. "What are you waiting for? Come here and make Harvey's cage ready for him."

"Yes, Mrs. Black," laughed James and Amy as they leaped to their feet and hurried to do just that.

coming soon

DUCKLING DIARY

by Ben M. Baglio

It was almost six weeks ago that she and James first spotted the duck building her nest. Two weeks to build it . . . four weeks to sit on the eggs. She looked at the dates, carefully written down since that first day. Her heart pounded with excitement as she worked the dates out.

She ran downstairs to the phone and quickly dialed James's number.

"James," she said before he'd even had a chance to say hello. "The eggs. They're due to hatch tomorrow!"

"Tomorrow!" James said. "That's great!"

"Come over as early as you can," Mandy said.

"I will," James said. "Definitely."

The following morning, Mandy was up bright and early. The warm mist promised another fine spring day. She waited eagerly at the gate for James and soon spotted him rushing down the street. Blackie was bounding ahead of James.

"Won't it be great if the eggs really do hatch today?" James's voice was full of excitement.

"Yes!" Mandy said. "My book said incubation varies from twenty-eight to thirty days. Today's the twenty-eighth day, I'm sure. So let's keep our fingers crossed."

When they approached the pond, they suddenly heard a terrible, frantic quacking and a splashing of water. Then a beating of wings. They saw a duck fly up and away toward the cornfield, shrieking in terror.

Mandy looked at James in horror. "That's our duck!" she cried. "Quick!"

They ran as fast as they could through the long grass toward the pond.

At the water's edge, a terrible scene met their eyes. Mandy's hand flew to her mouth, and she stood there in stunned silence.

"Oh, no!" James exclaimed in a horrified voice.

The little bankside island was empty. It *was* the mother duck they had seen. Her nest had been destroyed, and she had flown away. There was no sign of the eggs. All that was left were reeds and twigs floating around the island in sad little bundles.

"Poor duck!" Mandy wailed. "What will she do now?" Tears rolled down her cheeks.

Blackie came and licked her hand. He always seemed to know when people were upset.

James was almost crying, too. "Who could have done it?" he asked, shaking his head.

Suddenly, Blackie bounded off toward the little island. There didn't seem to be much point in going after him. The duck had been frightened away already. Blackie sniffed around in the long grass for a minute and then came trotting back.

Mandy was still sobbing.

"I bet it was a fox," James said.

"Yes," Mandy agreed tearfully. "I know foxes have to eat, but why did a fox have to attack *our* duck?"

Blackie placed something on the grass in front of Mandy. Then he nudged her knee. It was an egg. A duck egg. A perfect, unbroken duck egg.

Forgetting her tears, Mandy picked it up and cradled it gently in her hands. It was still warm! "Oh, James," she whispered.

James stared at the egg and gave Blackie a big hug. "Good boy, Blackie!"

"James," Mandy said urgently. "Do you remember when Libby Masters's pet hen, Rhonda, was hatching her chicks? Rhonda could only leave the eggs for a few minutes, otherwise they would get cold, and the chicks inside would die."

James nodded. "Yes," he said. "We've got to keep this egg warm and get it somewhere it can stay warm as fast as we can, so the baby duck inside doesn't die."

"Grandma and Grandpa are closest," Mandy said.

"Right," James replied. "Come on!"

With Mandy holding the egg in both hands close to her body for warmth, they hurried toward Lilac Cottage.

Grandpa was surprised to see the three of them so early in the day, although he had been up for a long time. He was in his greenhouse tying up a web of string to support his budding tomato plants. Grandma had just gone out shopping.

"What on earth's wrong?" Grandpa asked when he saw their anxious faces.

"Oh, Grandpa!" Mandy quickly told him what had happened. "Where can we put the egg to keep it warm?"

"The linen closet should do for the time being," Grandpa replied.

They all hurried indoors. Mandy walked carefully up the stairs and placed the egg on a bundle of Grandma's snowy white towels on the shelf nearest the hot water tank.

"That should do it," she murmured. She touched the shell gently with her fingertip. "Now you keep nice and warm, baby duck. We're going to look after you, so you needn't worry." She closed the linen closet door softly and ran back downstairs.

Grandpa and James were sitting at the kitchen table.

"Well," Grandpa said. "Now what are you going to do?"